CONQUEST OF SPACE
AND TIME . . .

THE RAILWAY

THE FIRST BRITISH MAIN LINE DIESEL-ELECTRIC LOCOMOTIVE, BUILT IN 1947 BY THE LONDON, MIDLAND AND SCOTTISH RAILWAY. IT IS HERE SEEN AT THE HEAD OF A SOUTHERN REGION EXPRESS FROM WATERLOO TO EXETER.

CONQUEST OF SPACE AND TIME

THE
RAILWAY

By

EDGAR B. SCHIELDROP, C.E., D.Sc.

*Professor of Applied Mathematics, Oslo
University, Member of the Academy of
Science and of the Committee of the Society
of Engineers, Norway*

Foreword by:

CECIL J. ALLEN, F.R.S.A., M.Inst.T., A.I.Loco.E.

LONDON
HUTCHINSON

Hutchinson & Co. (Publishers) Ltd.

178-202 Great Portland Street, London, W.1

London   Melbourne   Sydney   Auckland
Bombay   Johannesburg   New York   Toronto

First published in the English translation 1939
Revised and Enlarged Edition 1956

Printed in Great Britain by
WILLIAM BRENDON AND SON LTD
THE MAYFLOWER PRESS
(late of Plymouth)
WATFORD

CONTENTS

FOREWORD

EVERY now and again, in this atomic age, we hear that railways have had their day, and that the time has come for them to hand over their transport functions to the roads and to the air. Nothing could be further from the truth. While there certainly has been a fairly extensive closing down of unremunerative branch lines in Great Britain and the United States, it is a totally different matter with the remainder of the railway network. It may be agreed that railway saturation has been reached in many European countries, our own included, but it is not so in many of the world's undeveloped areas. In the wide region of Asia between the U.S.S.R. and China, for example, new railway construction is being carried out today on a considerable scale.

To those who have heard the claim that our railway rolling stock ought all to be scrapped, and the railways converted to motorways, it is amusing to visit a terminus like Waterloo at, say, the morning rush hour, and see its twenty-one platforms disgorging their tens of thousands of passengers; it is equally so to watch the endless procession of trains at stations like Clapham Junction or London Bridge, each handling over two thousand separate train movements every day. How many motorbuses or motorcoaches with their crews would be required to perform the same function, and even if they could be crowded on to the converted railway tracks, to what astronomical level might road casualties rise in consequence?

That the roads could deal with all the railway freight traffic is an even more ludicrous contention. How many lorries would be needed to absorb the one thousand tons of coal that can be carried in a single British freight train, manned by an engine-crew of two and a guard? Or what would be the road equivalent of some of the bigger modern American freight trains, with their quadruple-unit diesel-electric locomotives handling anything from 120 to 150 bogie wagons, very likely having a total weight of more than ten thousand tons? No; the railways are very far from ceasing to function. On the contrary, their managements in every country in the world are doing their utmost to increase the efficiency of their lines, the attractiveness of the employment that they offer, and the appeal of their services to the public, by making use of the most modern techniques in equipment, operation and administration.

In this book it is evident that Dr. Schieldrop takes the same view, and although the reader may not always agree with the author's estimates as to the probable course of future railway development, he can hardly fail to be stimulated by Dr. Schieldrop's evident enthusiasm for his subject. His is the broader survey rather than the detailed and technical examination, but it is always an approach that is tinged with respect and, indeed, admiration for all that the railways have done in the century-and-a-quarter of their history.

"Romance brings up the 9.15" is a familiar tag. In the pages that follow we are impressed, with the aid both of the author's text and his world-wide range of illustration, by the romance which has permeated the whole course of railway history from the earliest days until now, and which is not yet at an end. So this is a book well calculated to add many of its readers to the ranks of the railway enthusiasts, as well as to the users of the varied facilities which the railways provide, and I trust that it may succeed in both these aims.

CECIL J. ALLEN

CHAPTER I

RAILWAYS CONQUER THE WORLD

THE railway was invented before the age of steam. It was originally an economic roadway for horse-drawn vehicles, usually trucks laden with the products of mines and quarries. Its advantages and disadvantages were long debated, but its efficiency was finally demonstrated on the Grand Surrey Iron Railway in 1805, when a single horse, taken at random from a timber-cart, drew a total load of 55 tons for six miles along a level without distress. The 'road' consisted of two sets of metal angle-plates, one for each train of wheels. The combination of economy and efficiency was so outstanding that the establishment of the iron road as a permanent foundation for heavy transport may be fixed at that date. It is not likely to be superseded, in spite of the notion sometimes expressed by 'modern science' enthusiasts that the railways are now on the decline. On the contrary, they are developing with unprecedented rapidity, and remain the great and vital arteries of national and international economic life.

It is true that within the last few decades a dangerous rival has appeared in the motor vehicle, which already dominates the roads, and the shifting phases of the contest will be watched with eager interest by future generations. However, the railways are well armed for the fray, and many recent technical developments show that the day is yet distant when the road vehicle may aspire to conquer the realm of land transport. There are many, however, who look with misgivings on the large capital investments locked up in our railways, and consider that we should have fared better in the face of present-day problems if we had not engaged ourselves so deeply in the 'old-fashioned' means of transport. This opinion often goes hand in hand with lack of appreciation of the capacity for adaptation and development which the railways still possess. It is far from just to the railways, which have fulfilled their task hitherto with such efficiency.

The Grand Surrey Iron Railway, 1803–48, showing the embankment and bridge over the Chipstead Valley Road. This pioneer railway acquired the adjective "Grand" by popular usage; it was not in its original title.

Human civilization must always be mindful of its debt of gratitude to this unique wonder of engineering science—the railway. Immeasurable spiritual and material benefits have been conferred on mankind by the Iron Road during the century and a quarter since the sound of a train was first heard in the world. The railway has placed in the hands of mankind one of the mightiest weapons for its struggle for the domination of our world—an unparalleled means for conquest, development and expansion. Most important is the railway's ability to carry enormous loads unlimited distances without fatigue, and to do so at speeds undreamt of before its invention. The question of speed is of the utmost significance today, and the early pioneers did not fail to appreciate the coming need for faster and faster trains.

A contemporary sketch of the Rainhill Locomotive Trials, with Stephenson's *Rocket* leading. A reproduction of the original list of the competitors is shown opposite.

No 2-

LIVERPOOL, OCTOBER 5, 1829.

A LIST OF THE ENGINES

Entered to contend at RAINHILL, on the 6th of OCTOBER instant,

FOR

THE PREMIUM OF £500,

OFFERED BY

The Directors of the Liverpool and Manchester Rail-road,

FOR THE

BEST LOCOMOTIVE POWER.

No. 1.—Messrs. Braithwaite and Erickson, of London; " The Novelty ;"
  Copper and Blue; weight 2T. 15CWT.

2.—Mr. Ackworth, of Darlington; "The Sans Pareil;" Green, Yellow,
  and Black; weight 4T. 8CWT. 2Q.

3.—Mr. Robert Stephenson, Newcastle-upon-Tyne; " The Rocket ;"
  Yellow and Black, White Chimney; weight 4T. 3CWT.

4.—Mr. Brandreth, of Liverpool; " The Cycloped ;" weight 3 Tons ;
  worked by a Horse.

5.—Mr. Burstall, Edinburgh; " The Perseverance ;" Red Wheels ;
  weight 2T. 17CWT.

The Engines to be ready at Ten o'Clock on Tuesday Morning. The
Running Ground will be on the Manchester side of the Rainhill Bridge.
  The Load attached to each Engine will be three times the weight of the
Engine.
  No Person, except the Directors and Engineers will be permitted to
enter or cross the Rail-road.

J. U. RASTRICK, Esq., Stourbridge, C.E.
NICHOLAS WOOD, Esq., Killingworth, C.E. } Judges.
JOHN KENNEDY, Esq., Manchester,

Before the beginning of the machine age there was a definite upper limit to the speed which could be attained on land, and no traffic regulations were needed to maintain it. The natural speed limit was set by the horse. Nothing could go faster than the horse. By centuries and generations of specialized breeding, horses were finally developed which, over a short distance and a perfect track, could cover a thousand yards in 61 seconds, a speed of just under 40 m.p.h. This was the absolute peak. The world record for a trotting horse pulling a light vehicle, in 1806, was 20 m.p.h. Later developments, with pneumatic-tyred wheels and improved breeds of horses, brought this average up to about 30 m.p.h., which we may take as the absolute limit for animal transport.

Then, on the 6th October, 1829, was started one of the most interesting races the world has yet seen: the Rainhill Locomotive Trials. Four engineers, with four locomotive engines, took part in a competition arranged by the Manchester and Liverpool Railway. This race was, in fact, for a bigger prize than the £500 actually offered. The victorious engine made its designer not only the most famous man of his day, but also the pioneer of a new era.

Novelty, Sanspareil, Perseverance, and George Stephenson's *Rocket* (Robert Stephenson, his son and successor, was the nominal builder), were the names of the first four 'iron horses' which took part in the world's first race between mechanically-propelled vehicles, on that October day just a century and a quarter ago, over a distance of 22

The horse scores its last triumph over the mechanical vehicle, and wins by a head from a steam-driven locomotive on the Baltimore and Ohio Railroad in America, 1830. While congratulating the horse on a fine performance we may be glad that, on our side of the Atlantic, Stephenson's *Rocket* proved the superiority of mechanical transport.

Railway trains have a firm hold on the child's imagination. How many million toys have they inspired, from the simplest and clumsiest counterfeit of reality to the completely accurate and true-to-scale natural model! As far back as 1859 the little Prince Imperial of France had this toy railway built for him at St. Cloud.

miles 'on the Manchester side of Rainhill Bridge'. A fifth engine was entered, but was disqualified for cheating. The exceptional lack of smoke from Brandreth's *Cycloped* aroused suspicions, and it was found to be worked by a *horse concealed in the boiler*—an engine of literally one horse-power! It was disqualified after protest.

In the first race, the *Rocket* won the day. All the other competitors broke down and pleaded for another chance. They did no better, however, on the 8th, 13th, and 14th of October. *Rocket* won the trials and the prize, and made a complimentary run as the winner. In the trials, this engine hauled trucks weighing 20 tons in all—much more than the figure of 4 tons 3 cwt. required by the rules, which stipulated 'three times the weight of the engine'. Let loose on its own, *Rocket* raced away at an estimated 35 miles an hour.

Thus the mechanical vehicle had definitely and finally beaten the galloping horse. This is why we may—indeed must—consider the 14th October, 1829, as the opening of a new era, the age of mechanical transport, the first acceleration towards the conquest of space and time.

To the honour of the horse be it said that animal transport did not surrender forthwith, or without a struggle. In the 'outfield', elsewhere in Europe and in America, horse-traction continued for some years. Cooper's *Tom Thumb* on the Baltimore and Ohio Railroad was once raced by a horse—and *lost*! But the triumphs were short-lived. The horse had finally lost the battle for speed. In addition, after having survived its teething troubles the machine also won on endurance. It

One may question the taste which prompted this design for a coffee-percolator, but not the railway enthusiasm which produced it. When the water boils in the 'boiler' it is forced into the front compartment, where freshly-ground coffee awaits it. At the same time, the boiler tilts and douses the spirit lamp. This 'Cafetière Parisienne Toselli' is now a rarity.

was tireless; it had no physiological limitations—only technical ones. And the nature of these is still to be seen.

However, it is not the top speed under ideal conditions which is the decisive factor in traffic and transportation. Journey time is determined by many further factors, not least the skill and success displayed in organizing and utilizing the technical means available. Even during the long period in which, as we have seen, the horse dominated land traffic, journey speeds, and thus journey times, fluctuated quite considerably. The Romans had a road-system, extending over Europe, Africa and Asia, of roughly 50,000 miles in total length. In addition, however, they also had a highly-developed traffic organization, and journey speeds in Roman times were amazingly good and consistent. The distance from Antioch to Byzantium, 680 miles, was regularly covered in five or six days. Some despatch riders travelled up to 190 miles a day. In this connexion, an English gentleman-rider in 1831 covered 200 miles in 8 hours 42 minutes, but that was on a race track—and nineteen horses were used in completing the distance!

These are, however, peak figures. The average Roman despatch rider covered about 30 miles a day, day in, day out. After the collapse of the Roman Empire, this figure dropped, and did not rise again for many centuries. According to French statistics, a 'diligence' or mail-coach, on French roads, averaged 1·37 m.p.h. in the 17th century, and 2·11 m.p.h. at the close of the 18th century. In 1814, the average rose to 2·67 m.p.h., and by 1830 to 4·04 m.p.h., which roughly equals the Romans' 30 miles per day. By 1848, the French mail-coaches were averaging 5·9 m.p.h., but, at the same time, the London and Oxford coach in England was covering the 54¾ miles in 6 hours, nearly 9⅓ m.p.h. It had taken nearly two thousand years for the speed of land travel to equal that of the ancient Romans!

Immediately the superiority of the steam locomotive became established the construction of railways commenced on a grand scale.

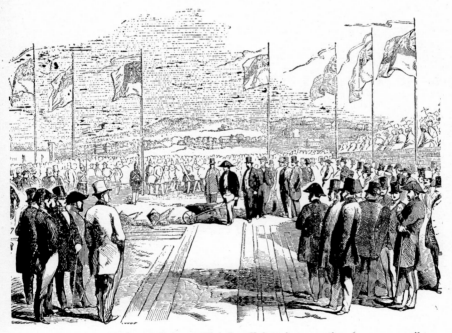

As a rule 'cutting the first sod' is considered sufficient inauguration for a new railway. Stadholder Severin Loevenskiold (Norway was then under Swedish rule) went further on 8th August, 1851, when he himself wheeled the first barrowload of soil at the opening of the first railway in Norway—the main line from Christiania (now Oslo) to Eidsvoll.

For a country to have no railway soon became a sign of backwardness and isolation, not only in the direct sense that it was cutting itself off from contact with the rest of the world, but also, and more significantly, because it became unable to match the pace set by advancing civilization. This factor is becoming increasingly important at the present day. Whoever cannot keep pace, either from inability or from fear of the consequences, is foredoomed to stagnation and oblivion.

Developments soon showed that the states and governments had well understood the signs of the times. The network of railways became closer and closer, and the combined length of the world's railway tracks is now well over 750,000 miles, sufficient to lay a 35-track railway right round the Equator. But when, relinquishing the dead language of mere mileages, we turn to examine the distances actually covered on the world's railways by the multitude of trains using them, the favourite yardstick of 'times round the world' fails us and we enter the region of truly astronomical magnitudes. For instance, the annual train mileage in the United States is 373 million miles, which is the distance from the Earth to the planet Saturn. The figure for the whole world is approximately 3,200 million miles—the distance from the Sun to the planet Neptune. Such distances may be difficult to conceive, but they do indicate the importance of the railways in world economy. The railways surround our Earth with many—and tight—bonds; they have shrunk its time-radius to about one-fiftieth of its former length. Thirty-five miles per day has become less than an hour's run.

The railway has opened up new countries and connected them with the rest of the world, has founded new cities and populated waste

This old G.W.R. engine, built in 1880, pulled the last broad gauge train in 1892. The broad gauge made for fast, smooth travel, 60 m.p.h. being often exceeded. These locomotives had driving wheels 8 ft. in diameter; some broad gauge engines had wheels up to 9 ft. diameter, which had no flanges and stood as high as the top of the boiler.

The builders of the railway from Lima across the Cordilleras, in order to master the natural difficulties of the terrain, had to drive an immense number of tunnels, no less than fifty, in one ten mile stretch. The picture, a view from the mouth of one tunnel into the next, gives some idea of the obstacles encountered in constructing this great landmark in the rich and eventful history of railway engineering.

lands; and this has been achieved in spite of the fact that the railway is neither particularly simple in construction, nor flexible in application. It is, in fact, somewhat exigent in its requirements, needing for its permanent way a firm foundation on levelled and solid ground, with easy gradients and wide curves. It is precisely such thorough preparation, however, which gives the railway its particular importance and its superiority over other forms of land transport. The obstacles are many: swamps and deserts, watercourses and snow, high mountains and dizzily deep valleys, but once the difficulties are overcome they are conquered for all time for the benefit of man. The punctual courses of the trains bring yet another new land into the rhythm of world traffic.

B

All this has been won at no little cost. Immense forces have been expended in this struggle against Nature's barriers; soaring capital sums have been invested in railway works, their rebuilding, repair and modernization. Figures alone, however, can tell little of the purely human contribution, the indomitable spirit, skill and ingenuity in overcoming obstacles, the physical endurance under stress and hardship, the inflexible will power under superhuman difficulties, which, in the first instance, have enabled this world-embracing labour to be completed.

The advance of the railway caused an upheaval—a revolution in the full sense of the word. But, to judge from the headshakings, the doubts and hidebound objections, even the enemies of the railway had no conception of the revolution that was to take place. *That* they could not imagine—not in their wildest dreams. On the contrary, the usual kind of objections, which do so much to hamper the course of the gold innovator, were raised, and as usual they centred round petty inconveniences, minor discomforts, trifling complaints. The opponents of the railway turned their thoughts in all directions. Their solicitude was all embracing.

"It would be most inconvenient for anyone to have a railway outside the window," said Sir Isaac Coffin in the Parliamentary Committee on railways. "What will happen to those who seek their

This train, drawn by *Best Friend*, a tiny, four-ton locomotive, inaugurated the first regular train service in the United States, on the 15th September, 1840, from Charleston on the then 'South Carolina Railroad'.

livelihood in the construction and maintenance of the highways?" he complained.

And, "What shall a man do if, like his fathers before him, he wishes to travel in his own, or a hired, private carriage? And what will happen to the saddlers and the carriage builders, the waggoners and coachmen, the innkeepers, the stable ostlers and the horsecopers? Has this House appreciated the amount of smoke, dust and noise which will be raised by this bustling locomotive? What man at the plough—what peaceful worker in his garden, could look upon this monster without horror? The iron prices will be doubled by the scarcity of this metal—a scarcity which is not to be avoided. The railway is the worst plague devised by human ingenuity, and it will reduce the lives of men to the utmost confusion."

Good Sir Isaac, typical representative of that class of hardy reactionaries who are always to be encountered in the world's history, doubtless thought that he had described exhaustively the anticipated horrors of the coming Railway Age. He overlooked one factor, however, not without importance. In addition to his peacefully working ploughmen and gardeners alongside the track, what of the wayfarer peacefully plodding along the permanent way? Others were not slow in envisaging him in their protests, however, and even foresaw 'cows on the line'. Even that prospect could not hold up the railway.

Such hidebound reaction inevitably created certain difficulties. Even after the very obstinate official opposition had been overcome, the first railway builders in Britain had great trouble in defending themselves against the assaults of angry landowners and farmers. Particular rancour was poured on the man with the theodolite—symbol of the horrors of progress. It became the custom, therefore, for a professional pugilist to accompany him in his work. The laying out of the line often had to be completed at night, by the light of lanterns, and guile and ingenuity displayed in order to mislead the opponents of the railway. One clergyman resolutely obstructed the surveying of the London and Birmingham Railway, peremptorily refusing the railway officials access to his glebe land. The surveyors finally forced an entry one Sunday morning, while the reverend gentleman was in his church and thus unable to defend his fields in person against these pioneers of a new and dangerous era.

Nowhere in the civilized world today is there such temerarious opposition to the advance of the railway. The lengthy arguments now circle around the pros and cons of plans and projects. Nobody now ignorantly sabotages railway development, but nevertheless in the

This typical American 'railway depot' of the sixties when Abraham Lincoln was President could comfortably be accommodated in our next picture . . .

arena of railway politics interests and opinions are often in violent collision. The many considerations which have determined the outcome in a particular case have not always been so well founded as to ensure that the efficiency of a railway system, its works and equipment, have remained beyond all technical criticism. Local and national interests are not always easily combined and agreement is often secured by compromises which do not exhibit a very high degree of technical prescience.

The engineer builds what he has been set to build, and takes his orders from the man who pays him. His task is to give form to an agreed plan, to lay his lines from point to point, as instructed. His field is not in the conference room or Parliamentary chamber. He fights his battles and wins his victories out in the open spaces. It is the forces of Nature which he must combat, and natural obstacles which he must overcome. The history of railway construction consists largely of accounts of the struggles of engineers and navvies with Nature itself. Many pages of this history witness to a stubborn endurance and selfless heroism which bear comparison with the most shining feats of war. Under all skies, the pick and shovel have broken ground in the endless crusade of civilization.

Africa was the last continent of the world to construct what is commonly described as a 'Transcontinental' railway: a railway from ocean to ocean. In 1931 the line from Benguela in Portuguese West Africa (Angola) to Elisabethville in the Belgian Congo, was finished.

Elisabethville, which lies on the 12th parallel of south latitude, nearly half-way between the Atlantic and the Indian Ocean, already had railway communication with Beira in Portuguese East Africa. There is now a continuous line of rails across the African Continent, but it is not possible to travel from coast to coast without changing carriages. This railway is anything but a direct line. From Elisabethville it runs nearly due south to Bulawayo in Southern Rhodesia, then northwards again in a wide sweep around Salisbury, to strike finally eastwards to the coast at Beira. As the crow flies, it is some 1,500 miles from Benguela on the Atlantic to Beira, but the railway is 2,950 miles long—nearly double the distance. This African line is the tenth transcontinental railway in the world outside Europe. There are four in the United States, two in Canada, one in South America, from Buenos Aires to Valparaiso, one through Siberia, and one in Australia, from Perth to Brisbane. These transcontinental railways have been the classic battle-grounds of the engineers' fight against Nature's hindrances. The difficulties the pioneers had to overcome were neither small nor few. When the older lines were built, modern technical resources were not yet available. What a gigantic task, already, was the laying out of these thousands of miles of track, through wilderness, across deserts and swamps, over wild mountain ranges, where often no human foot had

. . . the 'concourse' or waiting hall of Union Station in Presidential Washington.

trod before the surveying party broke through with their telescopes and ranging poles, seeking a clear and technically practicable route.

In these wastes, surveying parties disappeared and remained absent for months—many to return no more. They surrendered to sickness, hunger and thirst; they were attacked by wild beasts, or massacred by savage tribes. When the construction of the railway from Mombasa, a little north of Zanzibar, to Kisumu on Lake Victoria, had advanced to the Tsavo River, the lions declared war. They attacked the construction camps in such numbers and with such ferocity that for a long period, all work was interrupted. After every such attack by the lions, some ten or a dozen of the native labourers were missing, carried away by the animals into the depths of the bush. Uncontrollable panic fear overtook the natives. They threw down picks and shovels, and fled. The rumour of these terrors spread throughout the colony and it became almost impossible to hire new labour. Colonel Patterson, who organized the campaign against the lions, faced a difficult task. He has described it in his famous book, *The Maneaters of Tsavo*, one of the most exhilarating descriptions of tropical big-game hunting ever written. Finally, the lions were mastered, and labour returned to the camps. By then, however, the lions had slaughtered thirty of the imported Indian coolies. The number of killed and crippled native Africans was not even counted.

In many ways, the railways constructed in South America acquired a very bad reputation. The first attempt to build something in the nature of a transcontinental line was made by Henry Meiggs in 1870. It began with a railway from Callao, the seaport of Lima in Peru, up on to the highlands of Oroya, between the Western and Eastern ranges of the Cordilleras. The plan was then to connect the Pacific Coast of Peru with the navigable part of the Amazon River. As regards mileage, the major part in this transcontinental route would have been played by the Amazon: but, in other respects, the railway's task was not of the lightest. It was no child's play to find a route suitable for a railway train, from the sea level at the coast up to the high altitudes of the Andean chain. The mountain sides descended steeply from the needle-pointed peaks and sharp ridges to the depths of the valleys, smooth and frequently precipitous. The difficulties were great, even for the

---

Opposite we see how the railway from Lima in Peru, on the Pacific Coast, forced the steep, Cordillera range, breaking through finally at 15,694 feet above the sea, in the Galera tunnel, the highest in the world, and descending thence to the Amazon Basin. This gigantic feat was one long, obstinate and heroic battle against natural hindrances and climatic disease. Henry Meiggs, the pioneer, and seven thousand of his men died in this inhuman struggle. Truly it should be said of them that they 'fell in the field'.

boldest mountaineers, and considerably more numerous in point of fact, than any railway engineer could be expected to relish.

Meiggs did what he could. He blasted the way forward for his line of rails as long as the mountain side still gave him as much as a ledge to stand on. When even the ledge finished and the chasm yawned below, he turned and went uphill again, in a zig-zag, always up and up. Even the railways which climb about the Alps cannot show such a tangled network of twists and turns as the Oroya Railway.

A good impression of the natural obstacles on this line can be gained from the fact that fifty tunnels were required on one ten-mile stretch, and the monthly consumption of dynamite was 250 tons. When 6,000 feet above sea level had been reached, epidemic fever broke out, and men died like flies.

In 1877, after a seven-year struggle, the railway had fought its way through to the 12,000 feet level. Here Meiggs, the pioneer, died, worn out by the climate and the worry and responsibility of the gigantic undertaking. Eight thousand men had served under him, and barely a thousand survived. It had cost 7,000 human lives to lift the railway not twice that number of feet: two lives per yard. This casualty figure calls to mind the building of the first Panama Railway, under Ferdinand de Lesseps. There, malaria and yellow fever were the scourges, and there it was said that each sleeper in the permanent way had cost a life. Fourteen years after Meiggs' death, his railway was at last completed by the boring of the Galera tunnel, 15,694 feet above sea level—the world's highest. In the rarefied air of the mountain tops, work could only proceed for about three hours daily.

The first stage of the conversion of the G.W.R.'s broad gauge into narrow gauge track was the construction of 'mixed gauge' track along certain lines, thus enabling trains of either gauge to make through runs. The picture shows a broad gauge train travelling on a mixed gauge track.

One of the first railways in the United States—the City Point Railroad—with locomotive *Powhatan*, built in 1838 and weighing 7 tons. With its two driving wheels and nine-inch, inclined cylinders, this little 'tinpot' engine did not do so badly, hauling 150 tons up a gradient of 1 in 150 at 15 miles an hour.

The honour of undertaking the first truly 'gigantic' railway falls to the United States of America. In 1882, the U.S. Government approved the plans for a railway from Sacramento in California, on the Pacific Coast, across the Sierra Nevada and the Rocky Mountains, to the Mississippi River at Omaha, about 60 miles west of Chicago. In those days, it was no light venture to undertake the construction of 1,550 miles of main-line railway through such country. Since the undertaking could not raise its funds privately, State assistance was necessary. The State subsidies were greatly swollen by the so-called 'Land Grants'. The railway received the grant of a strip of land, 130 yards wide, along its whole length. In addition, for every mile of line a further grant was made of 3,000 acres of land, to be freely selected by the railway authorities with ten miles of the tracks. Distributed

George Stephenson is said to have hesitated between 4 feet 6 inches and 4 feet 8½ inches for the gauge of his first railway, the seventeen miles of line between Stockton and Darlington: a choice which became decisive for 470,000 miles of railway track in the world. This old locomotive, exhibited at the Festival of Britain in 1951, shows that the standard gauge, which many think ought to have been wider, afforded ample room for the locomotives of that day to be built with a very low centre of gravity.   .

over the whole length of the line, this corresponded to a strip five miles wide, all along the line. This system of land grants along the line of the railway has subsequently been used extensively in America. It can lead to paradoxical and even humorous consequences, as we shall presently observe.

The land grants, however, were not completely untied. In return, the State demanded preferential rates for troops, Government stores and the mails. The land areas thus passing into railway ownership were then valued at 125,000,000 dollars, but when the enactment concerning the preferential rates was repealed, some years ago, the railways secured a refund calculated at 1,250,000,000 dollars, or ten times the value they had already once received.

It will be obvious that, in an immense continent such as North America, the selection of the rail gauge was of major importance. In the 1860's, however, only very few people had the foresight to envisage an interconnecting network over the whole of the United States, with common use of many lines. Every railway company, each State of the Union, chose its own gauge, without considering its neighbours. Some lines had a 6 ft. gauge, some 5 ft. 6 in. In the Eastern States, the 'English' gauge predominated. This was 4 ft. 8½ in., as laid down by George Stephenson.

How Stephenson arrived at this gauge has been a matter for considerable speculation, although this distance of 4 ft. 8½ in. was to become, and to remain, one of the world's most important standard measures. Probably Stephenson never gave the matter very great thought—he had so many other things to do and to consider in building the world's first railways. It is highly unlikely, in any case, that Stephenson appreciated the gigantic scope of the problem. Had he realized the importance, both technical and economic, which would

The 'New Look' in locomotives. Little is seen of characteristic steam locomotive form. The austere, functional lines of the original *Green Diamond* diesel train on the Illinois Central system, however much they depart from convention, have a beauty all their own.

attach to it in time, he would surely have been overcome with his responsibility and long hesitated over his decision.

But how could Stephenson have known or realized that the task which lay before him was only superficially that of choosing a gauge for the mineral line between Stockton and Darlington, and that in reality it represented one of the most far-reaching decisions in the history of engineering? At the instant that Stephenson decided to lay these two rails, over a length of 17 miles, at a distance apart of 4 ft. 8½ in., he laid down for posterity a standard now maintained within a fraction of an inch over 470,000 miles of railway track throughout the world, and observed by some 150,000 locomotives and millions of railway vehicles.

It took some time, however, before the world as a whole bowed to the dictatorship of the 'Standard' gauge. In Britain, locomotive builders found this gauge too small. It was not suitable for the powerful locomotives which were increasingly favoured by constructors, and the companies began to lay their rails to suit themselves. Soon Britain had a profusion of gauges, and the famous engineer, Isambard Brunel, claimed the record with 7 ft. for the Great Western Railway, of which the last remnant from Paddington to Penzance, remained in use until 1892. However, as the British railway system became more closely knit, it was obvious to all parties that agreement on a standard gauge was an inescapable necessity. The only question at issue was: "Which gauge?"

Finally it was necessary for Parliament to intervene, and in 1845 a Commission was appointed to study the question. After hearing the report of this commission, Parliament took the decision. All future railways, and all under construction in Britain, were required to be built to Stephenson's gauge. Infringements were penalized at the rate of six pounds sterling per mile, for every day the gauge remained unchanged. Already, in 1837, Germany had built the first railway, between Nurnberg and Furth, to this standard gauge, which was thus introduced on the Continent of Europe and is now used by 60 per cent of all the world's railways.

A standard railway gauge, enabling joint running over extensive, connected systems, is, of course, a matter of the greatest importance. Apart from Russia, Finland and the Iberian Peninsula, we now have in Europe a connected system in operation.

Two ages meet on the opposite page: the Great Wall of China, in its day also an engineering marvel, built to keep the world out but now broken through by the railway, created by the modern spirit to keep the world together.

We give below a table of the principal railway gauges which, with one exception, are still in use.

NOTABLE RAILWAY GAUGES
Grouped as Broad, Standard and Narrow

Gauge	*Countries*
5′ 6″	India (and Pakistan), Ceylon, Spain, Portugal, Argentina, Chile.
5′ 3″	Ireland, S. Australia, Victoria (Australia), Brazil.
5′ 0″	U.S.S.R., Finland.
4′ 8½″ (Standard)	Europe (excepting U.S.S.R., Finland, Spain, Portugal, Ireland); also Canada, U.S.A., Mexico, Egypt, Algeria, Morocco, Turkey, Australia (principally N.S.W. and Commonwealth Trans-continental), China.
3′ 6″	Queensland, S. and W. Australia, Tasmania, Union of South Africa, East Africa, Rhodesia, Gold Coast, Nigeria, Sudan, Japan, Indonesia, Sweden, Norway ('narrow' gauge, now only on the Setesdalen Railway).
3′ 5¼″	Parts of Asia Minor, Algeria.
3′ 3⅜″	India (and Pakistan), S. America, E. and W. Africa, Burma, Malaya, Siam, Indochina, Norway (Thamshavn Railway, Graakallen Railway), Switzerland (Rhaetian, Montreux-Ober-land, Bernois and minor lines).
3′ 0″	Ireland (Donegal and minor lines).
2′ 11″	Sweden (minor lines).
2′ 5½″	India, Ceylon, Norway (Urskog-Hoeland Railway).
1′ 11½″	Wales (Festiniog and Talyllyn Railways), India (Gwalior State),
1′ 3″	Romney, Hythe and Dymchurch and Ravenglass and Eskdale Railways.

Whether this arbitrarily chosen 'Standard' gauge is in fact the most suitable is quite another question. Continued discussion of this matter serves no useful purpose now, however, since at this stage it is quite beyond the realms of possibility to make any change. It is true that, on a railway in Canada, a force of 2,720 men altered 340 miles of railway to standard gauge in one day, without causing any interruption of traffic. It is most unlikely, however, that all the States of Europe could be persuaded to agree to such a drastic alteration. Stephenson was in fact fortunate in being unable to appreciate the far-reaching consequences of his decision. We must thank George Stephenson for one thing, however, in that, early in his career as a railway engineer, he insisted on a uniform gauge, having the foresight to realise that later on they would all be joined together in one network of lines. With a gauge of 4 ft. 8½ in. the small locomotive boiler of early days had more than enough room between the wheels and it was the

The railway breaks through over the boundless American prairie.

same with the carriages. Things have changed since then. In order to accommodate modern, giant boilers on the underframe, it has been found necessary to raise them high above rail level. If a change of gauge were possible today, it might well be in the direction of greater width.

It will be plain now that this question of gauge is too complicated and many-sided to be dealt with in the compass of a popular exposition. For instance, it is not strictly true to assert that a narrower gauge does not allow of working heavy trains and powerful locomotives. On the South African Railways, locomotives up to 200 tons total weight are run on a 'narrow' gauge of 3 ft. 6 in. Even a step lower, on the 'metre' gauge (3 ft. 3⅜ in.), locomotives with tender weighing up to 150 tons are run, and very heavy stock is used on even narrower gauges.

The important and portentous question of the gauge became particularly prominent in America, when the first transcontinental railways were being built. Conditions should actually have been more favourable in this regard in the United States than in Europe. Here was no collection of independent national states which, owing to persistent rivalries, could reach agreement only with the greatest difficulty. North America, on the contrary, presented a union of states with an over-riding, powerful, central authority. Even in this case, however, as so often happens in the history of engineering, rational, technically-sound considerations received small attention and were apt to be pushed aside by other interests.

The engineers saw the most favourable prospects in a railway from the Missouri River eastwards to the Atlantic States, *i.e.*, connecting with lines on the British gauge. Accordingly, this was selected. At the other end of the Transcontinental line, however, California had its own railway system with a gauge of 5 ft. A long and violent struggle ensued. President Lincoln, finding it difficult to resist political pressure from a State with so many potential voters, attempted to settle the dispute in favour of the State of California and against the railway companies. He ordered, therefore, that the gauge should be 5 ft. The result was a disastrous 'break of gauge' at the Missouri River, which put a stop to any through running across the North American continent. In the face of the Presidential decision, the dispute continued to rage. Congress itself intervened, and prescribed the British gauge. The railway was built accordingly and the solution was undoubtedly the right one, considering the circumstances at the time. It is another question

A picture of the heroic age of railway construction, when, in addition to natural hindrances, Indians defending their hunting-grounds had to be dealt with.

whether American railway engineers of today would not have opted for the 5 ft. gauge, and had all other lines rebuilt to conform. At all events, designers of the subsequent American giant locomotives have sadly regretted the lack of these extra $3\frac{1}{2}$ in. in width. Such a decision was quite impossible, on economic grounds alone, at the time that the decision had to be taken. The State of California and President Lincoln were thus not in fact justified when they decided in favour of the 5 ft. gauge. A solution may be perfect from the technical aspect and yet economically impracticable. It may be necessary to make a limited sacrifice of principle in order to attain an immediate objective. It is this art of limitation which makes technical solutions economically practicable.

The first sod of the new railway was cut at Sacramento, California, on the 22nd February, 1863. The Eastern partner, however, the Union Pacific Railroad, could not get started. No sooner was the question of the gauges settled than a new and more violent quarrel broke out. This concerned the Missouri railhead of the line. President Lincoln chose a place with the odd name of Council Bluffs, directly across the river from Omaha. From an engineering viewpoint, the site was unfortunately chosen, and the railway builders preferred Bellevue, a few miles to the South. Events developed to the point that construction was started from Bellevue, flatly in the face of the President's decision, and some 100,000 dollars were expended before Lincoln forced the company to stop and recommence construction from Council Bluffs on the 2nd December, 1863.

When the Civil War between North and South began, new difficulties immediately arose. All costs rocketed upwards, and labour was soon in short supply. The line of the Union Pacific ran through a wilderness where practically no construction materials were to be obtained. Some 6,000,000 railroad ties or sleepers which were required had to be brought from Pennsylvania and Michigan, hundreds of miles away. Three hundred and fifty thousand tons of rails had to be hauled over the same distance by ox teams, at a cost that was itself ruinous, quite apart from the fact that delivery dates were unpredictable.

While the railway was passing through relatively populous and civilized regions, conditions were still bearable. But when the wide-open spaces of the prairies were reached, a difficulty arose to which no one as yet had given much thought. Hitherto, the Indians of the plains had been held in check by the U.S. Army but now that all the troops had gone to 'The War' the redskins could raid at will. They did not welcome the iron road to their hunting grounds. They attacked with all their resources. Large hordes hung around the tracks, shot at anyone exposing himself, wrecked the line at unguarded points and plundered the depots. The construction gangs had literally to fight their way forward, winning and holding mile by mile against the enemy. At a signal from the lookout posts, men threw down picks and shovels, grabbed rifles kept by in readiness, and took cover behind trucks or banks. It proved progressively difficult to maintain a normal rate of progress, when each hour's work had to be fought for, rifle in hand.

The engineers were at a loss and sought counsel from those experienced in fighting the Indians. Colonel North, a well-known figure on the prairie frontier, came to the rescue and found a cunning way out. Following the approved model popularized in the stories of Fenimore Cooper and Mayne Reid, he persuaded the Pawnee Indians to take up the fight against their ancestral foes and the disturbers of the railway—our old boyhood friends, the Sioux. The two Indian peoples gave battle, the Pawnees being more frequently the victors. Meanwhile the construction gangs drove ahead as fast as they could. The Sioux Indians thereupon changed their tactics. Instead of pursuing the regular attacks on the well-armed construction gangs, they started a treacherous guerilla warfare up and down the line. They did damage where they could, held up supply trucks, killed the crews, and plundered supplies. It was impossible to continue work in peace until General Grant himself visited the chiefs of the Sioux in their camps, and joined them in smoking the pipe of peace.

On the Western side, where the Central Pacific Railroad was responsible for construction, no such obstacles were encountered and work continued steadily. The line advanced up the Western slopes of the Sierra Nevada, following the watercourses, reached summit level at 7,000 ft. above sea level, and continued across the wilderness of the canyons to the barren lands of Nevada. From there, the line continued smoothly to the Great Salt Lake.

On this stretch, events took an exceedingly comical turn. Both railway companies, the company building from the East and that building from the West, had secured agreements with the United States Government for land grants. These had, in fact, been doubled to 5,700 acres per mile of track. At first it had been agreed that the Union Pacific should build on from the Missouri River westwards to the Eastern boundary of California, there to connect with the Central Pacific. Later, the Central Pacific obtained permission to continue building eastwards until meeting the other company. It was in the interest of both companies, of course, to build as many miles of line as possible before making contact and both therefore pressed forward with the utmost despatch.

'The last rail is laid, the last spike driven home. The Pacific Railroad is finished', was the message that went forth from Promontory in Utah, on 10th of May, 1869, over all telegraph wires, announcing the completion of the biggest feat of railway engineering hitherto performed in the world—the forging of the first railway link right across the American Continent.

In the winter of 1869, the two competitors met in Western Utah. They should then have bolted together their lines of rails from East and West as quickly as possible, and celebrated the occasion with grand festivities in the customary manner. However, what happened was something very different. The two construction columns redoubled their pace when they met and continued track-laying, apparently refusing to acknowledge each others' existence. They passed each other at speed, one going West and the other going East. We cannot help wondering how the engineers on either side managed to keep their men working thus, in sight of each other. Presumably they were only interested in the payout—'the more days, the more dollars'. They could, in fact, only be in pocket as a result of this fantastic decision of their employers.

The situation was certainly unique in engineering history. Stopping the advance of these toiling gangs, gripped by a mad urge, proved to be not so easy. Congress met to debate ways and means of checking this senseless race but the politicians found no way out. The companies themselves soon discovered that the cost of this farcical competition was becoming somewhat too excessive. By then, however, they had already built some 225 miles of double track. At last, on the 10th May, 1869, three years and six months after work had started, the last nut was

Hard labour for railway trains—old style. Four locomotives, puffing and blowing, steaming and smoking, were required in earlier days to hoist this train by main force up the steep climb to Soldier Summit in Utah. Now look at the picture on the opposite page.

tightened, the last spike driven home, and the band of steel between the Missouri and the Pacific was complete. Now indeed festivities began in the good old style and with every justification. Heavy traffic could now move from the Atlantic to the Pacific without the long voyage round Cape Horn.

With typical American accuracy and passion for figures, this was hailed as the third greatest event in American history, following on the Declaration of Independence in 1776 and the Emancipation of the slaves in 1865.

If we stand on the permanent way and look about us, the laborious care with which the whole structure has been assembled, from the drainage culverts to the rail joints, is at once plainly manifest. In fact it may well appear that a great deal of the work has been unnecessarily complicated. The gradients are so easy that we hardly feel them as we walk along the line, the curves so wide and sweeping as to be barely noticeable. Was all this really necessary? Could the line not have been built more easily, more cheaply, with steeper gradients and sharper curves?

For a quick and conclusive answer, take a ride on the footplate of an engine. As the train gathers speed and we stand in the jolting, swaying cab, we begin to acquire some understanding of the importance of substantial and careful construction. Looking forward through the 'spectacle glasses' or cab windows, we no longer feel that it is 'too safe'. An enormous boiler, a large steam engine underneath, so many heavy lumps of metal, all being hurled forward over a pair of rails which no longer appear to be at all too strong. On the contrary, they look quite dangerously flimsy. At each curve, the engine throws itself sideways, swaying and rocking. It does not seem possible that this slender structure of two thin rails, spiked to wooden sleepers lying bedded in angular stones, can hold together. A modern aircraft taking off does not give the same impression of hurtling power as an express locomotive.

Now we begin to see why the railway engineers, when building the track for their trains, are so careful and cautious, both in regard to gradients and to curves. Among all means of traction, a locomotive is

Hard labour for railway trains—new style. A quadruple-unit diesel locomotive hauls a long goods train over a difficult stretch of line in Southern California without any outward signs of distress. Only half the train is included in the picture.

that hauling the greatest weight for its size, and this is possible only by virtue of the adhesion of smooth-tyred wheels on smooth, polished rails. All that enables a locomotive to draw its train is the friction or 'adhesion' of its wheels on the rails. This makes the railway very sensitive to gradients. An incline which a motor car, with its ribbed, rubber tyres firmly gripping a tarmac or similar surface, can take in its course, is too steep for a railway train. Steeper gradients than 1 in 30, say those up to 1 in 27 or 1 in 23, which are to be found, exceptionally, on some European railways, present a difficult problem for the engine driver and are expensive for the railway companies.

Any incline over 1 in 50 is doubtful economy. At 25 m.p.h., such a slope requires seven times the tractive power needed on the level. A gradient of 1 in 200, on the other hand, only calls for three times the power needed on the level. Electric locomotives hold the rails better. It is an electric railway, the Chamonix line in the French Alps, which has the steepest gradient in the world, for a pure adhesion railway, of 1 in 11, between Chedde and Servoz. In Norway, the climb out of Oslo to Bryn Station is 1 in 40. On the Swiss main lines through the Alps, lengthy gradients of 1 in 37 to 1 in 40 are common.

Nor does the railwayman like sharp curves. As speed increases, requirements in this regard become more stringent. A radius smaller than about 300 yards is undesirable, and such a curve should not be entered directly from the straight. A suitable reverse curve should be used to afford an easy transition. Rules and regulations in various countries give definite guidance to which the railway engineer must strictly conform when laying out the line.

It cannot be denied that all these very stringent requirements are greatly at variance with the character of the country over which most of the world's railways have to run. The more credit is due therefore to the skill and ingenuity of the railway engineer, the more wonderful appears his ability to find a way out, or a way round, both in the literal sense. Speaking generally, the areas of our planet now assigned to human habitation are hardly ideal for such a means of transport as the railway. Mars might well be preferable as good railway country. There are, of course, many places on the Earth's surface where it is possible strictly to apply the prescription of Tsar Nicholas of Russia, who, it is said, took a ruler and drew a straight line between two points, stating, "that's how I want the railway to go". This tale may be true, but either the Tsar thought better of it later or his engineers deceived him, because the track of the line between what was then St. Petersburg and Moscow is not as straight as all that, although it must have cost large sums to take the line directly through the Valdai Hills. The

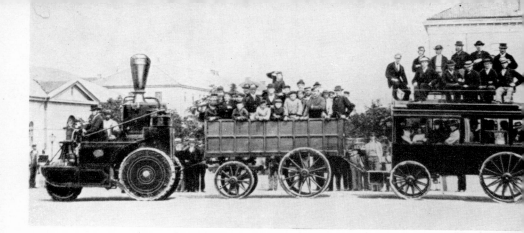

A Norwegian road-train put on trail by W. L. Rode at Gudbrandsdalen in 1871. The journey can hardly have been comfortable on the wooden carriage wheels! Road-trains proved too hazardous for serious development, though we have in the modern 'rail-bus' a single-coach vehicle that can leave the rails for the highway when necessary. See Chapter VII.

longest straight stretch of railway in the world is to be found on the Transcontinental Railway in Australia, over the Nullarbor Plain. On this stretch, the line changes direction once only and is otherwise dead straight for 328 miles, or about the distance from London to Edinburgh. In Norway, the longest straight stretches are in the tunnels: 5.65 miles in Kvineshei Tunnel, 5.1 miles in Hegebostad.

As a matter of fact, unless it is essential, it is preferable not to lay a perfectly straight course but always to give the line a slight sweep or curvature. This may appear odd but it is in fact so. We know, of course, that a train is held to the rails by the flanges on the inside of the wheels, which bear on the inner edge of the rail head when the train swings sideways. The profiles of the flange and the rail are arranged to fit each other, so that the wheel rises slightly off the rail when pressing against it. A certain amount of clearance is, of course, necessary. Thus, on a dead straight line, the train will be inclined to yaw, swinging from side to side, and the resulting oscillations can make for uncomfortable riding, especially if the wheel-flanges are worn. By giving the line a slight swing one way or the other, the wheels on one side are always pressing against that rail (the outer one) and help to steady the train.

The pioneers who laid the tracks for the first trunk lines, *e.g.*, the first transcontinental railways, were not always able to consider all these refinements of gradient, curvature, and permanent way dimensions, which would be essential, nowadays, for a really well-built railway line. The cost was in any case so enormous that all other considerations had to give way to the one over-riding consideration: to build as quickly and as cheaply as possible. It would have been quite impossible to

An artist's impression of the first trial run of a train in Norway—on 4th July, 1853, from 'the paddock at Oslo Goods Yard to the Point near Strömmen, a distance of 2 Norwegian miles (12½ English miles)'. The journey took 31 minutes 'although the train stopped on the way to take in water and was further impeded by people refusing to leave the rails'. The open, third-class carriage is considerably placed in front of the engine. *Robert Stephenson*, which was the name of the engine, was followed by the 'First-Class Coach', distinguished equally by elegance and comfort, and finally the Second-Class Carriage, which in both respects is slightly inferior. This was the first train on the Oslo-Eidsvoll Railway, opened for traffic on 1st September, 1854.

raise sufficient capital at the outset to build the railway according to the more stringent regulations introduced subsequently.

Even the cheapest railway was so costly that it was essential to get traffic going as quickly as possible, and thus avoid leaving the large invested capital lying idle any longer than was absolutely necessary. In consequence, the construction programme evolved for a railway dispensed as far as practicable with all costly cuttings, tunnels and similar earthworks, avoided large bridge spans, and, where bridges were unavoidable, built them as cheaply as possible. By this method of avoiding or evading natural obstacles and building quickly, remarkable results were in fact obtained. One of the first contractors for America's first trunk line, Oak Ames, built 435 miles of line in one year. Such a policy, however, increased the length of line necessary and, therefore, the running times. With cheap construction considerations of security are inevitably overriden, and operating and maintenance costs pared to the minimum.

In time, the effect of this policy made itself felt in the first trunk lines, the construction of which we have been following. The companies went bankrupt, even though the volume of traffic exceeded even the boldest expectations. The whole vast undertaking, with all permanent way structures and rolling stock, was auctioned in one lot. This auction, probably the greatest in financial history, was held outside the goods depot at Omaha on the 1st November, 1879, and the hammer fell on a bid of 45,000,000 dollars.

That was indeed a low price, and the new railway company was therefore able to embark on building-period No. 2—reconstruction and realignment on a large scale in the interests of operating efficiency. Instead of obstacles being avoided, they were overcome. One straightening of the line which was undertaken in order to save some twelve miles in distance necessitated the removal of 4,000,000 cubic yards of earth and cost 2,250,000 dollars. The old, low-grade ballast (the gravel or granite chips in which the sleepers lie bedded) was removed and replaced by Sherman gravel, which was later found to contain several shillingsworth of gold per ton. Wooden bridges and trestles were torn down and replaced by iron or steel structures.

The most complete realignment was made at the Great Salt Lake. This immense sheet of water was one of the obstacles which the first alignment had evaded. Small wonder, since the lake is some 35 miles long in a line from Ogden on the East to the opposite shore. The track was originally deflected round the North of the lake into a grim mountainous region. Here it climbed up to 5,000 ft. above sea level, switchbacking over the steepest gradients. Even the most powerful locomotives could not cross this section at a greater speed than about 12 m.p.h. Tsar Nicholas with his ruler might have saved $43\frac{1}{2}$ miles from a total of 147, but that would have involved the impossible feat of carrying the line for a distance of 35 miles straight over the Salt Lake. But such impossibilities must be overcome in the battle with distance.

The ruler was applied, the railway aligned to fit, and a long trestle viaduct or bridge was built over the Great Salt Lake, to become the world's longest bridge. It was not a cheap structure, since the surrounding country is practically treeless and timber in outsize scantlings had to be brought from the forests of Louisiana and California. When the two arms of the bridge met in the middle of the lake, 38,356 wooden piles had been rammed, equivalent to a square mile of plantation. Once more, at enormous cost, distance had been conquered. And now, many years later, as the old piling is nearing the end of its life, and has to carry far heavier loads and higher speeds than formerly, the Southern Pacific Railway is setting about the tremendous task of converting the trestle viaduct to a solid stone causeway.

In another part of the track 35 miles were rebuilt at great expense without saving even a mile in length, merely to reduce the original gradient of 1 in 54 to one of 1 in 122. With the former gradient, fifteen powerful banking locomotives were kept in steam to help trains up the grade, returning light, 35 miles downhill. These were now superfluous and the journey time was reduced, but the extra cost was 10,500,000 dollars, in addition to the original cost of constructing the line. In another case, over 7,000,000 dollars were spent on a stretch of 42 miles to save twenty minutes in the running time of an express train— 'spending millions to save minutes'. The winning of these 'twenty minutes' involved the removal of 13,000,000 cubic yards of rock and earth with 2,000 tons of dynamite, and in addition, 65 new bridges were built with spans between 33 and 1,500 ft., requiring 170,000 cubic yards of concrete.

Obviously a high-speed world, in which so much is expended on saving a few minutes! These twenty minutes cost at that time about £1,500 per second, which must be multiplied by ten to correspond to present-day values. Time is money and this is the exchange rate in the age of speed.

CHAPTER II

OVER HILL AND DALE

THROUGH wild, undeveloped country the railway engineer generally uses such means as Nature has provided. He follows the valleys and the mountain slopes. As long as the valley bottom ascends evenly and gently his task is easy, but all too often the ground rises far more rapidly than the railway can follow. Advance is then only possible by spreading the rise over a greater distance. Frequently the line crosses and recrosses the valley or gorge, on bridges or viaducts, and, when this is insufficient, it may be necessary to pierce a projecting ridge with a tunnel to avoid a long detour. If even this does not suffice, the line can be taken round a turn or two inside the mountain in a so-called spiral tunnel, to emerge into the light of day higher up the mountain slope, although perhaps directly above the original entry.

Even the obvious can be done in a variety of ways. If the engineer needs to push the railway forward along a very narrow, V-shaped gorge, the number of ways in which he can achieve this is surprising. The various solutions which can be put forward will not greatly differ one from another, but they will differ, and their selection tests the art and ingenuity so essential in engineering. Among the many, or few, possible solutions of an engineering problem, the best and the worst will differ quite considerably.

A good example of this is to be found in the alignment of the Western Pacific Railroad between San Francisco and Salt Lake City, through the Feather River Canyon. At first the intention was to take the Central Pacific Railroad already mentioned, the first American transcontinental line, through this gorge. This alignment offered distinct advantages from the engineering aspect. It crossed the Sierra Nevada range at an altitude some 2,000 ft. lower than the ultimate summit-level of the Central Pacific line, and it is a considerable advantage not to require to lift trains a further 2,000 ft. up.

This project was abandoned, however, at the start. "Nobody but a madman would ever think of running a railway through the Feather River Canyon", said Huntington, the railway king. And there were many who said he was right. The problem was to take a line of rails through a valley which, for some 150 miles, is a mere cleft in the mountain with high, almost perpendicular rock walls on each side. At the bottom of this crack a wild mountain stream boils and foams. In the spring floods, when the snow melts on the Sierras, the water rises to 46 ft. above its normal level. A gloomy air of desolation overhangs this canyon. Feather River, in its time, has brought death and destruction to thousands of gold-seeking adventurers who penetrated its forbidden wastes, tempted by the rumour of a lake of gold in its depths. Local names, such as 'Humbug Valley' and 'Last Chance Valley' bear witness to the hard fate of these pioneers.

Such a narrow, long gorge, winding and breaking its way through steep, rock faces, might be considered as destined by Nature itself to form an impregnable barrier to the railway engineer. Strange though it may seem, however, the many surveying parties which, year after year, braving toil and danger, forced the Feather River Canyon, brought back each a different solution of the alignment problem. One party returned with a suggestion for a line involving a steep gradient of 1 in 43. Another improved this to 1 in 74, while a third managed to keep the gradient down to 1 in 81. All had faith, however, yet all their plans were shelved. Nobody wanted to risk money in a project the cost of which might prove immeasurable. Suggestions continued to come forward, the estimates rising higher and higher as the gradients became flatter.

As a matter of fact, the plan finally realized was the most costly of all. The facts are that Jay Gould had meanwhile attained to his railway kingship, and he demanded of his construction engineers a line through the Feather River Canyon with a gradient not exceeding 1 in 100. He got it, at a price. For the first 75 miles, the railway could only be carried forward by blasting a shelf in the solid rock. No wonder construction costs soared to astronomical values. The money was not wasted, however. This was a true economy on a long term view.

But no matter how cleverly a railway line twists and turns in a narrow, mountain valley, there usually comes a time when all ingenuity is fruitless and, in order to get forward at all, it is necessary to go straight through the rock. Even the cleverest railway engineer cannot make his railway a mountaineer.

In Europe, it was the Alps which presented the first formidable barrier of this type to railway builders, and attempts to surmount this

An old woodcut shows the appalling difficulties which confronted the railway engineer in the first passage through the canyons of the Sierra Nevada. Their grimness is reflected even in the names of these bleak defiles: Death Valley, Black Hole, Last Chance. The picture shows the line of the (old) Denver and Rio Grande Railroad, which was finished in 1889.

A tunnel is a hole in which a railway passes through a mountain. That sounds simple, but in practice it is not so simple. Sometimes the line burrows into the mountain only to come out again on the same side. It seems a foolish procedure but is often the only means available of gaining height. This is shown on the above picture of the Flaam Railway in Norway, on the climb from Kaardal, the highest habitation on the mountain, to Myrdal station. The line can be traced from the bottom, left-hand corner, hidden in a snowshed, and going into a spiral tunnel. It comes out of the tunnel on to a ledge in the middle of the left-hand side of the picture, and we see it again, 'one storey higher'. To master the small rise between the first and the third storeys, the railway line has run over a mile and a half in a loop, 1,476 yards of which lie in the longest tunnel on the line, Naali. Including a loop outside the picture, below, and the Bergen Railway at the top, running from Myrdal Station (top right), behind the Myrdal mountain, we have the railway on five levels. The highway on the extreme right makes the ascent in twenty-one sharp bends.

tremendous obstacle have produced some of the world's masterpieces of civil engineering. The penetration of the Alpine *massif* by a railway is no task for a novice. It is the more remarkable, therefore, that plans and projects for Alpine railway crossings date back to the earliest 'prentice years of railway engineering'. Already in 1838, a certain Swiss, Colonel Lanicca, boldly planned a railway across the Alps, through the Splügen Pass, at an altitude of 7,000 ft. Lanicca was before his time, however, and it was an Austrian, Ghega, who in 1854 had the honour of building the first Transalpine railway. This was the Semmering Railway, crossing the Eastern end of the mountain chain known as the Noric Alps. This first European mountain railway was a pioneer in many respects. It was the first railway to use spirals and switchbacks to gain height.

In the Alps, however, it is not enough merely to work one's way forward, to make use of the passes and mountain saddles. If the alignment is to be technically practicable the time comes when one must go through. The Alps have become the happy hunting ground of the tunnel builder, and display a collection of holes which must be unique in the world. There is no longer any particular thrill in burrowing through the earth in this fashion. But, while the layman might think that this is only due to the possibilities opened up by modern technical progress and resources, it is surprising to learn that already in 1857, engineers planned to pierce Mont Cenis with a tunnel seven and a half miles long. And this was to be by hand-drilling, in the days before dynamite and gelignite (blasting gelatine). The men who undertook this gigantic task must have had unlimited patience and perseverance, or they could never have found courage to continue when they measured the result of the first week's work—just 23 feet! This was certainly no great distance and there were still 40,000 feet to go—say $7\frac{1}{2}$ miles of hard rock. At that rate the tunnel would have taken 40 years to complete. But under pressure of necessity the men of Mont Cenis began to learn how to drill rock. An engineer named Sommeiller built special rock-drills for the work and the tunnel was finished in 14 years, the rate being just over 900 yards a year. The steady improvement in drilling machinery was reflected in the rate of progress in subsequent tunnels. The monthly maximum in the Mont Cenis was $99\frac{1}{2}$ yards, in the St. Gotthard 201 yards, in Arlberg 213 yards, and in Loetschberg, 338 yards. It must be remembered, however, that in the meantime explosives had also greatly improved. In boring the Mont Cenis tunnel, neither dynamite nor gelignite was used.

A famous old Alpine crossing is the Brenner Pass. It is also the easiest, since it is the lowest saddle in the whole mountain chain. Here, the first railway over the Alps was laid, the Brenner Railway, and this is the only Transalpine line which has no large tunnel-works. It crosses its highest point (4,496 ft. above sea level) in the open. This has obvious advantages, particularly as concerns the comfort of the passengers. Frequent long tunnels do nothing to increase the joys of a railway journey. On the other hand, to avoid tunnelling the Brenner line has a long stiff climb.

We may now ask whether the high cost of tunnelling is justified by the advantage of crossing the mountain at a lower level. The answer is that additional height is also expensive, both in construction, and, more particularly, in operation, owing to the necessity for lifting many heavy trains to a higher level. The problem for the engineer is also complicated for many factors are involved in deciding the exact point for the best crossing. It is interesting to see how, in the famed Alpine crossings, lower altitudes are often obtained at the price of longer tunnels. This is clearly shown by the following table, in which the height above sea-level and the length of the tunnel are given.

ALPINE TUNNELS

	Height above sea-level (feet)	Length of tunnel (yards)
Arlberg (Switzerland-Austria)	4,301	11,199
Mont Cenis (Switzerland-France)	4,259	14,948
Loetschberg (Switzerland)	4,067	15,980
Gotthard (Switzerland)	3,786	16,411
Simplon (Switzerland-Italy)	2,310	21,657 (12⅓ miles)

Tunnels are of course always expensive, but true economy does not necessarily consist in avoiding high costs. There is no simple rule, but experience shows that there comes inevitably a time when previous skimping of expenditure is bitterly regretted. Sometimes a realignment has to be made and more money is spent replacing a higher, shorter tunnel at a lower altitude. Thus, on the line from Basle to Olten (in Switzerland) the old Hauenstein Tunnel, 2,729 yards long at an altitude of 1,844 feet, was replaced in 1915 by a tunnel over five miles long, of which the north portal is only 1,361 feet above sea-level. Each foot of height saved thus cost over 4 yards of tunnel. Although the distances by the old and new lines are almost identical, the new easy gradients have made possible substantial accelerations between Basle and Olten. A plan is also now being considered to replace the Mont Cenis tunnel by a new one. The old tunnel is, as already mentioned, 4,246 feet above sea-level and about 7½ miles long. This may be replaced by a tunnel at 3,611 feet, but it would be nearly 14 miles long. If we except the tunnels of London's underground railway, one of which is 17¼ miles long, this would be the longest tunnel in the world, and about 1⅓ miles longer than the Simplon Tunnel.

Before work can be started on a tunnel, there is some most interesting and intricate preparatory work to be done. The problem is solved in a most accurate and ingenious manner. The two ends of the tunnel are

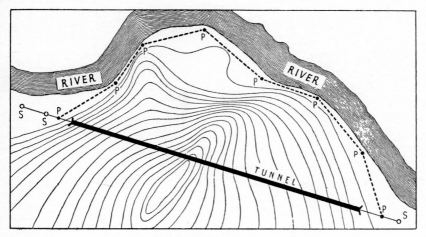

Surveying the line before drilling a tunnel.

more or less accurately located on the mountain slopes outside. In the case of the Simplon Tunnel, these ends were 12½ miles apart. Between them lies the high and inaccessible mountain. Drilling is started at a determined point from both ends simultaneously, and the working parties have to meet somewhere inside the rock mass. The problem is so to guide the work from the two ends as to ensure a proper meeting.

To this end, a 'polygon' of successive sighting lines is laid off from one end of the tunnel, round or over the mountain, along the most convenient route, to the other end or tunnel mouth. This line is plotted on the map as shown in the drawing above. The separate angles along this many-sided 'trace' are marked P in the drawing. Thus, measured points on the ground show the direction of each section of the trace, and the angles which the sections form with each other. In addition, the rise or gradient from each angle to the next has been carefully measured. Now it is possible in the first place to fix the angle which the centre-line of the tunnel must make with the first and the last sides of this polygon. Furthermore, we know the difference in level between each point P and any other point, and thus the slope from one tunnel mouth to the other. The centre-line of the tunnel can, therefore, be sighted and marked off on the ground, with the correct direction and slope. Two stakes, marked S, S on the left of the drawing, are placed in the line of the intended centre-line of the tunnel. A telescope is placed on the outer stake, and aimed over the top of the next stake, so that the line of sight of the telescope is correctly in line with the intended axis of the tunnel. A man now goes forward with a light or lantern, to the

D

position on the mountain side where the tunnel mouth is to be, and is guided until the light is in line with the sighting stakes. That is where digging or drilling begins. Having advanced a little way into the mountain, a second light is hung from the tunnel roof, and sighted on the stakes and the first light, in the same way. This is repeated as often as necessary. At a suitable distance along the tunnel, new, fixed sighting points are set up inside, from which sighting can go forward into the mountain, with the same telescope and new lights.

In principle, this is all very simple, but in practice the utmost care must be taken to ensure absolute accuracy, and this is not so simple. A mistake once made affects all following sights. As the costly hole burrows further and further into the mountain, by drilling and blasting, everything depends on the engineer's keeping true to the line. The final test of correctness will come on the day when the thin rock wall between the two halves of the tunnel, the 'headings', is broken down and the tunnel is through.

This is the load of responsibility to be borne by the engineer. Opinions may be aired, situations discussed, reams of paper filled and calculations developed, until that one day when the test comes. The engineer is always faced by the problem of having to forecast future happenings and give definite, accurate and irrevocable decisions. He

The Severn Tunnel—the world's longest underwater railway tunnel. Once a month the 'roof-tapping gangs' shown here examine the tunnel throughout its entire length of 4 miles 628 yards. The tunnel is ventilated by powerful fans, and pumps remove about 20,000,000 gallons of water daily.

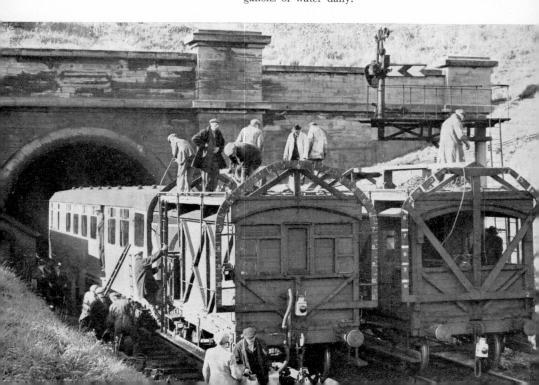

Tunnel digging with a 'shield'. This can be driven forward by hydraulic rams abutting against the finished portion of the tunnel lining. The method is used in soft ground; for example, for the London underground railways.

prophesies and guarantees that the two gangs will meet somewhere in the mountain, and one day everybody will know whether he has been right or wrong.

It is interesting to see how accurate the engineers have been when driving their tunnels, and some examples are given in the following table. This shows the divergence in height and alignment, but also the difference in length, *i.e.*, the gap between the tunnel-length according to the engineer's drawings and the real length.

ACCURACY IN TUNNELLING

Year	*Tunnel*	*Length* (*miles*)	*Length Error* (*feet*)	*Divergence Horizontal* (*inches*)	*Vertical* (*inches*)
1870	*Mont Cenis*	$7\frac{1}{2}$	46	*nil*	11.81
1880	*St. Gotthard*	$9\frac{1}{4}$	23	13	1.97
1905	*Simplon*	$12\frac{1}{4}$	2' 8"	7.9	3.54
1911	*Loetschberg*	9	1' $3\frac{1}{8}$"	10.24	3.94
1902	*Gravehalsen* (Norway)	$3\frac{1}{4}$	*nil*	1.57	*nil*
1940	*Kvineshei* (Norway)	$5\frac{3}{4}$	$9\frac{1}{2}$	4.33	1.97

A considerable triumph was that of the two Swiss engineers, Mathys and Baeschlin, who guided the drillers in the Loetschberg tunnel, the latest of the Swiss perforations of the Alps. This was completed in 1911, providing the long-awaited connexion between Central Switzerland and the Simplon line, and thus better communication between London and Paris on the one hand, and the plains of Northern Italy on the other.

During the construction of the Loetschberg tunnel, one of the most famous and interesting to be bored, an exceptional difficulty arose in laying out the course. After the drillers had penetrated about $1\frac{1}{2}$ miles into the rock, one of those terrible accidents so frequent in the history of tunnelling occurred, and blocked all progress in the original direction. The catastrophe itself will be described presently. Sufficient to say here that it forced the drillers to swing away from the straight alignment, and make a bend in what was considered to be a safer direction. In its final shape, therefore, the tunnel had a considerable twist. Starting from the northern portal, it first runs 1,312 yards straight ahead, then diverges for 875 yards, takes a 1,203-yard bend to the left, continues for not quite 7 miles on the straight, and comes into the light of day on the south side of the mountains after a right-hand curve of 328 yards, and a final spurt of 438 yards on the straight. In spite of these complications the two headings met so accurately that a final check showed a difference of 1 ft. $3\frac{1}{8}$ in. in horizontal distance, and not quite 4 in. in height, a very good result in a twisting tunnel 9 miles long.

Sinister and frightening forces dwell in these mountain depths, and woe to the poor human who releases them, when boring his way through the heart of the rock. The reports on the building of the Simplon Tunnel say:

"According to the original calculation boring of the tunnel should have been finished by November, 1903. At the rate at which the work was already proceeding, however, an even earlier finish was anticipated, but, after an advance of some three and three-quarter miles from the northern portal, the temperature of the rock suddenly rose to such a height as to upset all calculations. During the fourth mile, a temperature of 96–98° Fahrenheit had been anticipated, but it was actually found to be 113–118°. Six hundred yards farther on it rose to 127° and appeared to be still rising. Blowing in

This picture of the tunnel at Anseremme, near Dinant on the Meuse, gives a vivid impression of the enormous weight which the rocks forming the roof of a tunnel may have to support—or transmit to the tunnel-walls by virtue of their arched form.

The picture opposite shows the 'clearance gauge', built to the maximum dimensions of all vehicles used on the line. No part of a tunnel or bridge may project inward so as to touch it, and no part of a vehicle or load may project beyond its outline.

cold air was no longer sufficient; special water sprays had to be provided, which discharged icy showers to cool the air sufficiently to enable work to be resumed. While heat thus hampered the work in the North, on the South side it was rock pressure and water-bursts which, for a while, practically stopped all advance. The pressure of the mountain was tremendous; thick timbers splintered and strong steel girders were bent and twisted. Only by the use of mighty concrete pillars was it possible to hold off the pitiless pressure of the rock. Springs of cold and hot water burst into the heading, often so suddenly that many men were buried by the falling rock. They lie where they died, in heroes' graves, and their gravestone is the mightiest of all, the whole, towering height of Mont Simplon."

As already mentioned, the Loetschberg Tunnel enjoys the melancholy fame of having experienced the most appalling and tragic catastrophe in all the history of tunnelling. According to expert geologists, no particular difficulties were to be feared in driving this tunnel. The geologists were of the opinion that after the surface had been penetrated good, solid rock would be found. Their assumptions were wrong. On the 24th June, 1908, after a bed of limestone had been pierced,

At two o'clock in the morning, on the 31st March, 1911, the two headings met at the middle of the nine-mile long, Loetschberg Tunnel. This was the 'joyful moment', as the report has it, to which these lads had been looking forward for a thousand days of toil and danger.

The Woodhead tunnel between Manchester and Sheffield during construction, 1951.

nearly 3,000 yards within the mountain, the catastrophe occurred. At half past two in the morning the last shot fired broke through the rock-beds over the tunnel roof and brought down the whole bottom of the overlying valley, the Gasterental. This consisted of gravel and mud, saturated with water from the glaciers. Over 9,000 cubic yards of this oozing mass flowed through the blast hole and in *ten minutes* choked the tunnel heading for a length of nearly a mile. No fewer than twenty-four tunnel workers, overtaken by this avalanche, died in the tunnel. A few, who were farther off from the break and whose lamps had not been put out by the hurricane blast of the displaced air, barely escaped, fleeing with a torrent of mud lapping at their heels.

Both caution and economy indicated the necessity for a detour round these terrible masses of mud. Only one doubt remained: would it be possible, with this bend in the course of the tunnel, to lay off and lead the trace with sufficient accuracy to ensure meeting the other heading at a predetermined point? As already mentioned, these very considerable difficulties were duly overcome. Work was ultimately resumed; trial borings under the Kander River in the Gasteren Valley, along the new alignment to the 720-foot level, were satisfactory and at last, at the end of March, 1911, the final break-through took place.

It was two in the morning on the 31st March that one of the drills went through from the North side of the 30-inch rock-wall which still separated the headings. Such a break-through, after all the feverish tension of the days before, is an unique experience. Only the few concerned can really appreciate it. We quote, therefore, the words of the engineer who directed the work on the Northern side of the Loetschberg:

"We calculated the number of yards left again and again. That was, perhaps, a little unwise. The men grew more and more excited as the yardage fell. The eagerness to take part in the actual break-through increased, and the workmen themselves began to figure out which shift would be the lucky one. They tried to influence fate themselves by slowing down, even by making only a show of working, so that the great event should happen in their shift. Finally, we had to take steps to ensure that some work still got done. Now began a rivalry between the engineers themselves, which went so far that we had to make strict rules, and take steps to get things going again. Then came the day when the estimate showed only 43 feet left. Excitement gripped everybody, high and low. And what if Baeschlin had miscalculated? To tell the truth, we ourselves did not believe so whole-heartedly in our calculations; even Baeschlin kept protesting that it was impossible to be quite sure. On that day, we had to apologize for our doubts. On Thursday, the 30th March, at ten o'clock in the evening, we had fired a blast and waited, full of anticipation and nervous tension. Nothing happened. I sat down, pondering, and my thoughts were grim thoughts. The tunnel alignment must be out. At two o'clock, we drilled a 13-foot hole. Still nothing. I was feeling anything but happy. Then a man came running. 'Through!' he shouted, 'Through!' I could have cried with relief. But duty called, and then came the moment when Moreau, Chief Engineer on the work, pushed a bunch of flowers through the bore-hole, the nicest bunch of flowers I had had in my life. Moreau himself clambered through the widened hole, and the jubilant moments that followed cannot be properly described."

There does not appear to be any limit, within reason, to the length of tunnel which we can bore with modern resources. It is indeed difficult to set any limit, now that the problem of air-supply has been solved by boring two parallel tunnels. By cross-drifts from the one to the other at fixed intervals, which are later walled up, an efficient air circulation can be obtained. This was done in the Simplon. In the first stage, only one of the tunnels was bored to the full gauge; widening of the second, parallel tunnel was started in 1912, and finished in 1921, work having been suspended during the First World War. There is now a double-track line, with separate tunnels for each direction.

With the 12¼ miles of the tunnel, Europe at present holds the record for length in surface-railway tunnels. But it does not appear that this will be retained by her for long. Projects are now being considered in South America which will seriously imperil our lead in this regard. And the amount by which our record will be beaten will, apparently, be considerable. The railway lines between Argentina and Chile now pass over the Andes mountains, and there are good reasons justifying the substitution of a tunnel. Even if located in the most favourable place, the tunnel should be more than double the length of the Simplon; it would be 28 miles long. Meanwhile, complete plans already exist in Europe for a tunnel which would beat the projected American record by 5 to 6 miles—a tunnel under the English Channel between Dover and Calais. The prospects of this tunnel are, however, debatable.

It will be remembered that this project has hitherto been held up by the British desire to remain an island. But assuredly the last war will have shown that in the present air-age, 'splendid isolation' is impracticable. Technically, such a tunnel is quite within the bounds of possibility. It would not even be necessary to start with the traditional

The George Washington Bridge over the Hudson River in New York.

A fine, twilight picture of the grand arch of Sydney Harbour Bridge. With a free span of 550 yards, it is only some 25 feet shorter than the world's longest arch bridge, the Kill van Kull Bridge at Bayonne, New Jersey.

'first sod'. That has already been dug. As far back as 1869, the work was well in hand, and pilot headings several miles long had been driven on either side. These have been kept in order up to the present day.

According to the plans, the line would leave the railway from Paris at Marquise, South of Calais, and at once enter a tunnel which, at Sangatte, would begin to pass under the sea. The further course would not be a completely straight line, but would follow a route under the sea-bed most suitable from the geological point of view. The tunnel would come to the surface again somewhere between Dover and Folkestone. The line was planned as a double one, with two separate tunnels of 20 feet in diameter each, spaced about 65 feet apart.

Two more tunnels would be needed to keep the running tunnels free from water. These drainage galleries would lead into sumps on the English and French sides, out of which the water could be pumped. The actual tunnel would be 33 miles long and would shorten the running time between London and Paris by $1\frac{1}{2}$ hours. The traffic expected would be about fifteen trains daily in each direction. It should be added that as a result of a recent review of the future of air-transport between Britain and the Continent, the Ministry of Transport has decided that the tunnel would not justify the cost of its construction, and it seems that the project may be shelved for economic reasons.

Another submarine tunnel which may be constructed in the near future is the long-contemplated tunnel under the Bosphorus between Scutari North and Roumeli Hissar. The construction of the Bosphorus tunnel would probably lead, as an offshoot, to tunnelling under the Suez Canal. By these means, Europe, Asia and Africa would be knit together by an unbroken railway system.

Not only has the railway to burrow through hard rocks, but it also has to cross obstacles of quite different nature, which may, however, be equally difficult to overcome. Mountain ranges block the way by their steepness and height, gorges and valleys by their depth and width. From the dark depths of a tunnel we may issue into the light of day through a hole in a steep cliff. Below is a giddy drop, separating us from the firm ground on the other side of a valley. It is impossible to fill in such a cleft in the earth. The only solution is to carry the heavy trains straight across. So we must build a bridge.

A tunnel lies hidden in the depths of the mountain. It may have taken ten or twelve years to build, but all that appears to result are two small black holes on the mountain side, and some minutes of greater or lesser discomfort for the train passengers. It is not the same with a bridge. This lies fully exposed to the light of day, possibly in some prominent position amidst imposing surroundings and scenery. Here requirements exceed mere utilitarian or technical demands. A bridge should not only throw its arch like a strong-bow, carrying the heavy loads imposed on it; it should also be a joy, or at least a pleasure, to the eye. This two-fold requirement is not easily fulfilled, since the aesthetic effect of a bridge depends not only on fine lines and harmonious proportions. It must be given a form, both as a whole and in detail, which faithfully and directly indicates the *work* it is doing and the manner in which it is being done—how, in fact, it carries its own weight and that of the moving traffic it bears and conveys safely to the other side.

When we look at a bridge such as that over Sydney Harbour, with its lattice-work of hundreds of steel bars, forming a mighty arch over the one-third of a mile of water which separates the north and south sides of the harbour, the impression conveyed can be attributed to many different elements. The main feature is, of course, the general form and outline of the arch, but almost as important is the manner in which the arch is horizontally spanned by the distinctive roadway, which, with a slight upward curve, hangs from the long, double row of vertical tie-rods.

An important part is played by the varying lengths of the lattice bars, the rhythm in which they grow in length from the crown of the arch to the abutments, the setting of the diagonals, and, in particular,

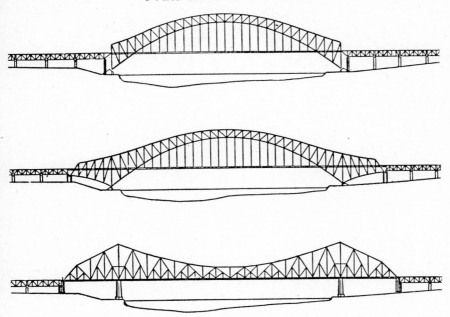

Different alternatives were suggested for the Sydney Harbour Bridge. These are shown, arranged in order of increasing cost. The topmost is best technically; the least satisfactory and the dearest is the last. On appearance, most people would grade them in the same order.

the width of the bars in elevation, from the observer's viewpoint. If a structure is pleasant in its general form and appearance, that is surely in great part due to the fact that it so obviously appears to be well and truly performing its duty. Sound, static calculation automatically incorporates important aesthetic values. This can be seen confirmed, at least to some extent, by an examination of the drawing at the top of this page, which shows the three projects submitted by the firm which won the contract for the Sydney Bridge.

Three different designs were put forward. At the bottom is a so-called 'cantilever truss', a heavy beam or girder formed of a lattice work of bars and rods and resting on the two central piers. The bridge girder does not finish there, however, but reaches over in two following spans (the 'cantilevers') to connect with the small viaducts which form the approaches to the bridge on either side. The upper design is an ordinary, two-hinge, arch truss. All three alternative designs solve the technical problem in that they afford an adequate means of crossing from side to side. In determining merit, the cost is the decisive factor, assuming that all the solutions are technically sound and acceptable.

A critical moment in the erection of the Quebec bridge in Canada; hoisting the central span between the two cantilevers. On 30th August, 1907, one of the cantilevers of the original design collapsed, and seventy-five men were killed. Of the second design, on 11th September, 1916, the central span had been raised as far as shown in the picture, when the hoisting gear broke and the whole span was dropped into the St. Lawrence River, to a depth of 38 fathoms. Finally, at the third attempt the span was safely hoisted into place.

Judged by the standard of cost, the projects must be graded as shown in the drawing on page 61.

The uppermost, the hinged truss, is the best; the lowest, the cantilever beam, the least satisfactory. The tenders submitted were for the following amounts:

Arch truss	..	..	..	£3,518,000
Cantilever arch	..	..	..	£3,748,000
Cantilever beam	..	..	..	£4,568,000

This was the purely technical assessment of the three systems proposed. Considering them aesthetically, judgment at once becomes more arbitrary, since the well-known proposition as to 'looks' versus 'utility' immediately comes into play, and tends to confuse the argument. It is impossible to doubt, however, that anyone comparing these drawings, and judging them as they appear to the eye, would arrange them in precisely the same order as the engineer who is judging on their technical merits only. From the aesthetic aspect, the choice between the soaring arch at the top, and the straight beam at the bottom, is obvious.

It is unnecessary to pursue this comparison further, since it only serves to illustrate the fact that sound aesthetic judgment usually coincides with sound engineering practice. Similarly, it is more than probable that a technically unsuccessful solution seldom looks well. This does not mean, however, that aesthetic considerations can be taken care of merely by attention to the technical aspects. Among the many factors deciding the appearance of a bridge there are several for which technical design offers a number of alternatives in the actual shaping and construction. A very simple, concrete example will serve to explain this. Calculations may show that a certain member of a bridge, say a suspension rod, is sufficiently strong to carry a load of 200 tons. If the material can be relied on to support a load of 1 ton per square inch of cross-sectional area, then, quite simply, the rod must

The four cables which carry the George Washington Bridge have each a diameter of 36 inches, and are twisted of cold-drawn galvanized steel wire, which can carry a load of 97 tons per square inch of cross-section before breaking. The total length of wire in the cables and suspensions is 108,000 miles (four to five times round the Equator). Its weight is 26,000 tons.

Timber carries timber in the Canadian forests. This wooden bridge is of the type called a
'trestle' in America. Formerly often used in Europe, it is now giving way to stone, steel and
concrete.

have a cross-section of at least 200 square inches, when it will reliably
support the applied load. What the calculation had determined is the
area of the cross-section of the rod. When standing and looking at a
bridge, however, what is seen is not the cross-section of the rod, but
only that flat side or face of it which is turned towards the observer. It
is the width of this face which decides whether this rod appears stout
or slender. If it is too slender, it appears ugly, since the observer inevitably gets the impression that the bridge has a weak spot at this point.
It is of little use then for the designer to explain that, 'statically', all is

On the next page we see an effective photograph of the George Washington Bridge, taken
from the top of one of the towers on the New York side, looking over to New Jersey. The
impression of height is perfect and the perspective decrease in the size of the motor cars on
the bridge gives a direct impression of the length. One of the eight traffic lanes will be seen to
be reserved for ambulance and emergency traffic.

satisfactory by virtue of the presence of certain steel plates which are not visible. It is what is actually seen which determines the *visual* sense of aesthetic fitness and balance, and which is as important for harmony in appearance as the 'static balance' for the safety of the bridge.

What has just been said applies to many features of bridge building. Within the scope of the static balance, there is, in reality, a wide field for variety of expression, and the designer must therefore have an artistic streak in his make-up if he intends to build not merely a bridge that will hold together, but one that can be seen and appreciated to be holding together. A prominent Swedish civil engineer and bridge-builder, Professor Linton, who has spoken and written so much on the difference between the mere building of bridges and the *art* of building bridges, sums up his views in the following phrase:

> "Just as an artist can change the expression on a portrait with a few strokes of the brush, it is possible, in designing bridge girders, to produce every impression, from that of sturdy strength under load, to that of extreme slackness and unfitness."

It is most praiseworthy of engineers to aim at making such dominating and monumental structures as their bridges as handsome as possible, but an absolute necessity is their complete mastery of the stern science of mathematical analysis and its application to the statics of structures. Looking more closely at any large bridge, we see enormous masses of steel sweeping in bold spans over wild ravines and broad rivers, and a vast tangle of criss-crossing beams and rods. Think of the millions of bolts and rivets holding the structure together at thousands of joints! Think further of the tremendous loads these bridges must carry, the masses of traffic which cross them—railway trains, motor cars and other vehicles; of the masses of snow which can collect on the bridge, of the storms which can beat against its wide surfaces, whistle round its piers and towers, and press on each separate rod and beam and plate. Well, then, may we ask the simple question: How can man's ingenuity and intellect disentangle these complicated happenings and relationships, this interplay of many forces? To this, the true and honest answer must be given.

Not all the world's best engineers, not all the methods of modern

---

Such bridges as the now seventy-year-old Forth Bridge will never be built again. It is sufficiently wonderful that the engineers and workers of those far-off days were able to erect such a maze of steelwork. It is true, they used 6½ million rivets, which alone weigh more than ten times the weight of the train shown steaming over. In one way, the Forth Bridge is well in the best tradition of British engineering. It is substantial and has withstood the most furious of gales without suffering any damage.

science have succeeded in penetrating and classifying this maze in all its details. This may come as a surprise to some people, though it will hardly cause them to forswear the use of bridges for the rest of their lives! They will think of the many thousands of bridges all over the world still unflinchingly carrying their loads—some for a century and more. It would appear that complete knowledge of all the concealed interplay of forces is not really necessary in order to build a good bridge. How, therefore, does one proceed to 'Calculate such a structure?'

Many will have wondered about this, and about the possibility of 'building' a complete bridge on paper and proving that this combination of many and varied pencil strokes will really be able to carry its intended load. Can we 'load' a drawing of a bridge with a railway

It is not possible to make an accurate, mathemetical calculation on paper, of such a complicated structure as a large bridge. For such a giant as the Kill van Kull Bridge, the longest steel arch span in the world, a model was made which was tested with model loads, representing the actual weights, traffic loads, wind pressures, vibrations, etc., in the laboratory. The work paid for itself. It is cheap and easy to make a whole set of models; once the Kill van Kull Bridge was built and in place, it would be too late to put anything right.

The top of one of the 745-foot towers of the Golden Gate suspension bridge, showing how the cable (encased in the tubes) rests on a curved 'track'. Each cable consists of 27,572 separate wires, and is required to bear a strain of 14,000 tons—the weight of a light aircraft carrier. A view of this bridge is shown on page 82.

train (also merely an image in pencil strokes), fully guarantee that the actual bridge of steel will be able to carry its own weight—let alone the weight of all the *real* trains which will run over it?

The problem can be solved within reasonable limits, and the actual designing is done in two stages. Statics, or the science of the balance of loads and forces, enables us to calculate how big a load, in tension or compression (stretching or crushing) will have to be carried by each member or part of the structure under the 'least favourable' conditions. When this is done, the next stage is to determine how heavy or big the beams, bars and plates will need to be in order to carry the calculated loads. Samples of the materials of which the bridge is to be built are sent to a 'Test House', where it is ascertained; for example, that any particular steel can stand a pull, or a crushing force, of so many tons per square inch of cross-section, before breaking. Thus, if a steel can withstand a pull of 32 tons per square inch, and it is to be used for a

Erection of the first all-aluminium bridge: the Saguenay River Bridge at Arvida, in Canada, an arch with a span of 289 feet. Aluminium is not as strong as steel, but it is so much lighter that aluminium alloy can compete with steel even in bridge construction.

bar or girder required to carry a load of 100 tons, then its cross-section must be about 3 square inches, since each square inch can carry 32 tons. But, if I were to learn of a bridge built to this calculation, I should prefer to use a boat! Such a bridge may survive, but will always be on the point of falling down, since even though the calculations may be correct the rods will be loaded to utmost capacity. Should, somehow, some day, a train with heavier passengers come along, the whole structure might collapse.

The engineer, whose training stresses the importance of knowing one's own limitations, reasons in another way. The Test House say that the rods will carry 32 tons per square inch without breaking. The engineer allows for them to carry only about a fifth of this, say 6 tons per square inch. He must have this margin of safety, since he cannot anticipate all that may happen. If he is to sleep quietly at night, after traffic has begun to roll over his bridge, he must be sure that, even if any particular piece is loaded to five times its calculated load, it will still hold fast. In other words, he is using a 'factor of safety' of 5.

This factor of safety may be considered as partly reflecting on the sufficiency of our knowledge and partly as an expression of our human striving after safety. It must not be rashly thought, however, that if one bridge is designed with a factor of safety of 5, another may require a factor of only 3. To feel safe while crossing the last-named bridge, one would first wish to make sure how the calculation has been made *before* the safety factor was applied to the dimensions. A business man would not think of considering one estimate better than another, only because the first one included a larger item for 'unforeseen expenses'. The decisive fact is how one has calculated and estimated all the *foreseeable* expenses.

It is exactly the same with the design of an engineering structure. In one country it may be customary to calculate with particular care, allowing for high wind pressures, taking account of vibration and shocks from the rolling wheels, etc. If the engineer takes sufficient care beforehand he may not need such a high factor of safety. Elsewhere, possibly, the practice is not to calculate so comprehensively and thoroughly, not to pay such attention to secondary details, but to multiply the calculated figures by a larger safety factor. These considerations apply to ordinary bridges. At or beyond the limit of existing experience, as with structures of exceptional type or large erections whose weight, size or span surpass those of all predecessors, only the most meticulous calculation covering all the factors that can be mathematically treated will be good enough.

In the calculation of a bridge structure, we are faced at the start with an obvious dilemma. A great part of the load which a bridge has to carry is represented by the weight of the structure itself. This weight, however, also depends on the size—the 'scantlings'—of the members of the structure, and that can only be determined after the calculation is finished. This appears to be a vicious circle. The dimensions of the

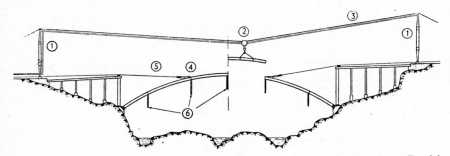

A sketch showing the erection of the aluminium bridge at Arvida in Canada. 1, Derrick masts; 2, Travelling crane lifting 7 tons; 3, 14-inch diameter conveyor cable; 4, 50-ton hydraulic hoist; 5, Ropes supporting the erected parts of the bridge; 6, Sighting poles, for levelling the structure.

The Kylling bridge near Warma, Norway.

structural members can only be determined when the weight of the bridge is known, and the weight of the bridge can only be determined when the dimensions of its parts are known. This apparently hopeless deadlock which can fortunately be easily solved by virtue of the fact that a great many bridges have already been built in the world, and a fund of experience has accumulated which it is both legitimate and sensible to utilize. Any bridge designer's office has weighty volumes of data on all existing types of bridges. From such tables, we can ascertain the probable weight of the projected bridge. If it is properly designed in detail, the weight should not differ excessively from the average for all existing bridges of the same span. When the bridge is finally designed, and the scantlings decided, the actual weight can be added up. If this does not agree too well with the weight assumed in the calculations, a suitable correction must be made.

It may now be asked why it is necessary to calculate and design afresh bridges for quite ordinary, standard spans? Why not

It hardly seems possible to put a new span in an old bridge without disturbing the traffic; but engineers have performed even this feat. The new span (on the right) is erected by the side of the old one, while traffic passes through unhindered. The old span is then pushed aside, to the left, the new span drawn into its place in the same manner, the rails connected up, and the next train can pass freely. Very, very simple, once the idea had been thought of and all the small details cleared up. As regards the old span, readers might like to think of some way of disposing of it, before turning the page.

This is the solution to the foregoing problem. The old span, replaced by a new one, is un-ceremoniously 'pushed overboard' into the Ohio River. The bridge is one at Cairo, Illinois.

decide on standard types for such and such spans and particular natural conditions? On practical grounds, a large organization such as a nationalized railway may find it useful to standardize some bridge-types for small spans. But a glance at the different illustrations in this work will surely convince the reader that the day is yet far distant when the collection of disconnected considerations which go to determine a particular bridge design can be reduced to a simple formula.

However, a bridge has not only to be calculated and designed. Its separate parts must be made in the workshops, the whole must be assembled on the site, and then the bridge must be erected. Many a design which looks so well on paper can never be realized, since, for certain technical or economic reasons, it might be impossible to erect such a bridge on that particular site. Having planned the hundreds of

An imposing view of the Forth Bridge—one of the junction points, where the giant, tubular girders meet. They were stout fellows, those who made all this hold together. It will be clear, now, why the total surface area of the steelwork in this bridge is nearly 124 acres, and that the painters have been going steadily from one end of the bridge to the other, and painting without a break, for seventy years, since 1883.

One of the side spans of the Fades Bridge is finished and the steel lattice work is now being extended, piece by piece, straight over the valley bottom 433 feet below. That this can be done without scaffolding is a triumph of engineering skill. We should admire, too, the men who work exposed to the weather at such dizzy heights.

component parts of his bridge, the engineer has further to decide how they are to be got into place—high up in the air, perhaps over water. Erection is a science in itself. It involves many difficult and interesting problems which, in course of time, have found many solutions.

An extremely neat solution of a not very simple erection problem is shown in a series of pictures of the remarkable Fades Bridge over the River Sioule, near the town of St. Eloy in the French department of Puy de Dome. The illustration below shows the completed bridge. It consists of three immense box girders of lattice construction, forming one continuous beam stretching between the abutments on the cliffs and passing over the two massive granite pillars on either side of the river. This beam is of substantial dimensions. The side visible to us is 40 feet deep, and the train, just passing over the bridge, appears therefore quite small in comparison. The total length is 420 yards; the central span, from pier to pier, 472 feet.

Let us consider the situation when the two abutments on the banks, and the two tall pillars or piers, are finished. We have now 'only' to lay the 420 yards long beam across these supports. It is obvious that it is impossible simply to build up the beam on the river banks and hoist it somehow into place. Even our much-vaunted engineering skill cannot produce sufficiently powerful cranes to do such work. Fortu-

The Fades Bridge over the Sioule River in the French department of Puy de Dome shows that French bridge designers, as well as French dress designers, understand elegance.

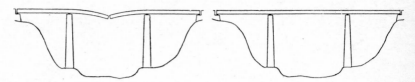

On the left, the girders of the Fades Bridge have been built forward from either side an
droop 'nose down'. In order to rivet them together, as shown on the right, the droopin
ends were hauled up by winches on the piers, so that the rivets could be driven. But—

nately a simpler method is available. A beginning can be made in th
gaps between the piers and the abutments. A wooden scaffolding can
be built up there on the slope. If necessary, this need not go the whol
way but only about half the distance. On this scaffolding we can
assemble the parts of the bridge girder from pieces made in the work
shops. We can build out from each abutment, right along the scaffolding
Then we build out into space! One stringer after another can be pushec
out over the end of the one before, like the parts of a telescope. The
sections can be pushed out on rollers, running on the part already
built. Thus, the bridge can advance gradually, from either side, acros
the gap. It may look like a daring rescue operation, but the work goe
forward.

In this manner, we move forward towards the bridge piers, while
counterweights on the abutments keep the girders from toppling over
Having thus reached the piers, we 'carry on' in the same manner righ
to the middle of the span, until the two halves meet, with slightly
sagging ends, somewhere in the middle of the main span, as shown in the
sketch accompanying. Heavy jacks—rather heavier than those known
to every car owner, but in principle the same—are now placed on the
piers, under the girders, to lift them until the tips meet. It only remain
to push in the last few bolts and rivets, and the bridge is joined up.

This does not prove so easy, however. The middle span of the
Fades Bridge is 472 feet long, and over such a length, a steel bar wil
stretch or expand, or contract or shorten, about two-thirds of an incl
for every 10 degrees of change in temperature. The rivet holes are
say, one inch in diameter. Assume that all the calculations are correc
and that everything has been properly done. Then the two halve
should meet with the rivet holes exactly in line with each other. How
ever, if the actual air temperature on the morning the bridge is finally
assembled is 10 degrees lower than was assumed in the calculation, the
rivet holes will not coincide; they will be just two-thirds of an incl
out, and the bridge cannot be riveted up.

In the case of the Fades Bridge, this was allowed for in the following

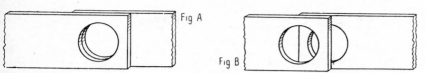

Fig A

Fig B

—even then, a gap remained (Fig. B). Only when the two halves of the girder had been sufficiently warmed by the sun did they expand until the rivet holes matched (Fig. A) and the connexion could be made.

way. The bridge runs nearly north and south. At dawn, when finally assembled, the rivet holes were out of line, as shown in Fig. B., above The sun rose in due course, and warmed the east side of the bridge. The girders on that side began to expand, and the rivet holes 'registered' by midday, so that the joint could be riveted up. On the 'shady' side, the situation was not quite so good. There was still a small gap. By using thinner rivets ($\frac{9}{16}$ inch) and a little force, the joint was made. Later, as the sun went to the West, that side also was warmed up sufficiently, and full sized (1 inch) rivets could be substituted for the provisional connexion. The bridge was now properly joined up.

In this record-breaking age the question will naturally be asked,

Bayonne Bridge, the longest arch bridge in the world, spans the 560 yards across the Kill van Kull river, between Richmond on Staten Island, and Bayonne in New Jersey.

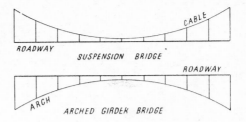

A suspension bridge is an arch bridge upside down. The cables and suspension rods are stretched, or loaded in *tension*, whereas the arch and abutments are *compressed*. This is important, since rods or bars in compression tend to collapse or *buckle*, and cannot carry such a heavy load as in tension.

how long can a bridge containing a *single span* be built? It is not easy to furnish the answer. It depends on conditions, and modern engineering science is full of surprises. The biggest bridge-arch hitherto built is the Kill van Kull Bridge, with a span of 560 yards. From this to the longest suspension bridge over the Golden Gate in San Francisco there is a big jump. The Golden Gate Bridge has a span of 1,400 yards, more than three-quarters of a mile.

Thus, for such long spans, the suspension bridge is far superior, and it may seem surprising that there should be such an immense difference between the suspension bridge and the arch. As the cut shows, a suspension bridge is just an arch turned the other way round. In the suspension bridge, the roadway is suspended on rods leading down from cables which hang in a curve. In the arch bridge, the roadway is carried on vertical struts which stand on the back of the arch. It is not at first sight clear why, if we can build suspension bridges with spans up to a mile long, we cannot throw an arch over the same distance. Most readers, even non-engineers, will have the feeling that somehow this cannot be done, though the reason may not be apparent.

A bar as thick as a match made of the steel used in the largest suspension bridges can carry a load of about 12 cwt. Observe: this load *hangs* from the bar. Reverse this arrangement. Take such a bar or rod, as thick as a match-stick, and use it as a walking-stick. If you lean hard on your 'stick' it will at once bend and break. Even the best steel on the market will do this. On calculating, we find that this steel rod which can carry a *pull* of 12 cwt. can support a *pressure* of only 13 lb.

This is the matter in a nutshell. In the suspension bridge, the cables work under tension, and even thin cables can carry large loads. In the arch, on the other hand, all parts are working under compression, and

---

Opposite, we see how the Bayonne Bridge looks when we are travelling along it, with the arch itself soaring above us. The roadway on which we are running hangs from steel rods on either side. The horizontal lattice work, seen both above and below, not only supports the roadway but also stiffens the bridge structure against side winds tending to overturn it. From its characteristic form, seen in the background as a series of K's lying down, the engineers call this a 'K-truss'.

F

Bridges often compete in sheer beauty with their natural surroundings. Over the Golden Gate the world's biggest bridge stretches its imposing span of 1,400 yards (nearly three quarters of a mile). Few technical structures can rival the beauty of such a suspension bridge, in which the roadway hangs from slender cables attached to towers each 745 feet high.

to prevent them from bending and collapsing such an arch must be made very big and heavy, if the span is large. Consequently, while the cables of a suspension bridge appear only as a thin streak on the landscape, the arch-bridge completely dominates its surroundings.

The theoretical limit of free span is approached at the point where the structure can bear its own weight, and no more. Such a bridge would not be of much practical use, however. The practical limit is, or course, lower. The Golden Gate Bridge is yet far from the theoretical limit. The free span is 1,400 yards. The towers are 745 feet high, and weigh 22,000 tons each. The cables of this bridge are themselves interesting. There are four of them, and each has been assembled in place from 27,572 separate wires, each of the thickness of a lead pencil. They run over the towers, resting upon them in heavy 'tracks' (see p. 69), with a force of 56,000 tons, the weight of a very large liner.

CHAPTER III

FROM TROPICAL SWAMP TO MOUNTAIN SNOW

A RAILWAY line need not be of any great length, need not span a continent from ocean to ocean, but may still have required a great deal of engineering skill and human labour. There are, in various parts of the world, a number of railways which cannot compare in sheer mileage with the imposing Transcontinental lines, but which have cost far more in human life and endeavour, and in the technical skill of their builders. A mile on the flat prairie is not the equivalent, for the pioneering railwayman, of a mile through the African bush, the wastes of the Sahara or the Alaskan snows.

On the Western coast of Africa, there is a region with the promising name of the Gold Coast. For miles, it is covered with thick, well-nigh impenetrable, fever-laden jungle—the 'Bush'—concealing in its depths slimy lagoons, stagnant waters and bottomless swamps, where deadly danger lurks at every step. This jungle belt extends as a close screen all along the coast, sometimes to a width of 180 miles. Courage and resolution are needed to penetrate this barrier. A few meandering tracks exist, trodden through the centuries by aboriginal feet. They give little help, however, to a surveyor forcing his way forward to trace out the line of a railway.

The first attempt to map on paper the *hinterland* of the Gold Coast ended in tragedy. A party of three, two engineers and a doctor, carved their way inland to lay out an approximate line. The ground in those parts is hidden under a thick layer of rotting vegetation, and the powerful tropic downpours soon convert this mattress of leaves, stems and other growths, into a yielding morass, covering ponds, and pot-holes. Here mosquitoes and other pests flourish; this is the home of tropical fevers—malaria and others—which are a surer shield to the country behind than the most warlike of cannibal tribes. The coura-geous little party soon met these defending tropical hordes. The mosquitoes displayed considerable strategy—they bit the doctor first. Then came the turn of the younger engineer, and the fever-ridden doctor could not save him. The other engineer took charge of the doctor and dragged him back toilsomely along the way they had come.

Things did not look too promising for the projected railway. The most subtle persuasion and the most tempting offers failed to find anybody willing to make a second attempt. There remained the one and only bait which has never failed to tempt men to brave all dangers, all climates, sickness and death itself, and which will encourage even the weariest to resume their burdens and press on. That tried and tested bait is—Gold. The river sands of the Gold Coast have that tempting, golden glitter. The pioneers followed the 'colours' upstream, and found the mother-lode at Tarkwa, some forty miles inland. The usual 'gold-rush' set in. Labour and capital flowed into the country. It proved difficult, however, to approach the tempting treasure; still more difficult to bring it back. All goods had to go on the heads and

Hard work under the pitiless African sun, on the railway from Dakar to the River Niger.

A railway of unique character once launched out from the Southern tip of the Florida Peninsula, and crossed the sea for 120 miles on a series of bridges between a chain of small islands. Over this marine railway, the 'Oversea Limited', sped towards Key West. Destroyed by a hurricane, this line has now given place to a roadway.

backs of natives, to and from the coast, and the transport charges took a big slice out of the profits.

And so, eventually, the railway came—had to come. It was pushed forward from a little bay on the coast, Sekondi. From there it was some forty miles to the mines of Tarkwa, but such miles as never a railwayman had had to deal with before. The jungle climate was not conducive to hard work. The mortality among the staff and the labourers was devastating. Even laying out the trace of the line was a special problem. It is not so easy to 'sight your marks' in the green twilight of the tropical jungle, which is so overgrown with creepers and bushes that a clear range of sight of thirty yards is an exception. In such country, a man must have 'a nose for a railway', must have the instinct to 'smell' his way along a suitable line.

Surveying in the tropics has one peculiar difficulty which is not encountered elsewhere. The line once sighted and cleared, stakes must be cut from the surrounding trees and driven in to mark it. But these stakes refuse to remain there and mark the line. They take root, they sprout, they grow. The line of stakes becomes a line of trees. In this tropical hothouse, every living part of a plant and cutting grows. When the time comes to start building the railway, the first clearing along the track is already overgrown, and the marker stakes have to be looked for and identified in the greenery. Hence, all the important reference points and lines have to be marked with something which will not sprout and grow—for instance, concrete blocks. Since the only means of transport in the thick bush are native porters, the need for economy in the use of concrete markers is obvious. Clearing and keeping clear of vegetation a finished railway line in the tropical jungle is a never-ending task. Trees shoot up to a fantastic size: perhaps twenty to thirty feet in diameter at the root, and 130 feet high. On the Gold Coast, an average of seventy or eighty such trees per mile had to be felled and removed with the most primitive methods: axe and fire. The work took a long time. The clearing in the forest was kept open for a width of 100 yards to prevent interference with traffic, but even that is not always sufficient. The Gold Coast Railway has some 200 stoppages each year from trees falling on the line. The roots hold badly in the loose, waterlogged soil, and the trees at the edge of the clearing lean inwards, towards the light, so that when they fall they fall across the line. Nor need

An Indian railway station. The 'Pakistan Special' on the point of leaving New Delhi. Quite a number of India's teeming millions appear to be on the platform to bid it farewell.

Natives boarding a train at a railway station in Dahomey, French West Africa. There are no platforms and no shelter but the trees, although the equator is less than five hundred miles away. Nevertheless, some enterprising souls have organized a 'refreshment bar' on the ground. The natives travel with their goods to market in these open trucks—presumably there are no 'reservations'!

it be imagined that such a clearing through the forest, once cut, remains open. The whole vegetation is steadily advancing on the railway from both sides, and must be held back in never-ending combat.

The construction work from Tarkwa onwards to Kumasi could only be carried on with native labour. No white workers were obtainable, nor would a white man have had much chance of surviving hard, physical labour in that climate. The labour force was about 16,000 men, an enormous number according to European standards. The harsh, economic rule in the tropics is, however, men—not machines. All went well until the great Ashanti rising broke out under the native

From Sheep Camp, the goldseekers start across the ill-starred Chilkoot Pass, the gateway to the fabulous Klondyke. Once, fifty men were buried in a snow fall at the foot of the pass. The number of all those who died on the way across the mountains, in that year 1898, when the gold fever drove venturesome men into Alaska's stormy frozen wastes, will never be known.

king, Prempah, then the whole labour force vanished; the men ran away, or deserted to the enemy.

The abandoned works quickly deteriorated. Things looked bad for the engineers in the advanced construction camps, and for the surveying parties pressing forward through the jungle far ahead. One of these parties was 'running the line' towards Kumasi. They knew nothing of the revolt and the little Colonial campaign that followed. They fought their way doggedly forward through the bush, and, all unknowing, approached the enemy stronghold, Kumasi. Day by day, they came nearer to certain death. However, luck did not desert them. When they finally broke through to Kumasi, they found the place, to their great surprise, occupied by a strong, British garrison. Only then they realized that if they had made better speed they would have fallen in with other, far more dangerous folk.

After seven years of hard and unremitting toil, the railway broke through to Kumasi. In this period, no less than ten Chief Engineers had relieved each other 'in the field': the terrible climate allowed no longer working life for each.

In 1867, the United States of America bought the territory of Alaska from the Russians. They paid £1,440,000, which to many people seemed an exorbitant price. If Russia wanted to buy back Alaska now, the price would have to be far, far higher. The original sum paid is a mere fraction of the wealth which has since been extracted from the country. The first adventurers, however, who attempted to tap Alaska's vast resources, at once made a depressing discovery: this treasure chamber was surrounded by a barrier of natural obstacles such as man has seldom encountered.

From an obscure little harbour, Valdez, on the south coast of Alaska and at the head of Prince William Sound, 3,000 men started in the late winter of 1898 to make their way inland in search of gold. This famous 'Gold Rush' brought death for the many and riches for the few. Behind Valdez, tall, ice-clad mountains rise, grim guardians of the Promised Land. The gold-seekers worked their way forward with horse teams, tents and mining equipment. Without experience and training in such Arctic travel these unfortunate pioneers easily became the prey

Over Alaska's snowy wastes, the train presses forward along the 475-mile line from Fairbanks to the Pacific Ocean.

of blizzards, fogs and frost. Snowstorms lasting five days are no rarity in these high latitudes. When the gold-diggers, after endless toil, reached the top, new trouble arose. No one had thought of such details as snow-blindness, or foreseen that the loose snow would allow travelling only by night when the surface froze hard enough to bear the weight of the horses. What such a burdened, crawling caravan looked like after some days in a raging blizzard can hardly be imagined. The wind and the snow swept men and horses away, whirled tents and gear into complete confusion. A few such experiences were enough for the many. Those who escaped turned back and crept wearily into Valdez again. A few did break through across the Chugach Range to establish a settlement which later became Copper Center, on the Copper River, but only to become decimated there by scurvy and other maladies.

A few tough individuals remained alive, however, whom sickness and hardships could not destroy. When the winter was over, they pressed forward again. They were both disappointed and rewarded. They did not find any of the gold which had lured them to venture, but they found 'bonanza'—copper deposits so rich and large that even the copper kings, the Morgans and the Guggenheims, had to take notice. It was soon obvious, however, that even a rich copper mine could not become a source of wealth without a railway from the coast. An immediate start was made with the subsequent 'Copper River and North-Western Railroad', one of the most daring railway projects in the world.

This railway passes through some very difficult country. Nearly all the possible difficulties of a railway engineer are encountered in turn: wild ravines, long stretches of swamp, raging rivers full of ice floes, quaking soils, floods, landslides, snowfalls, frost, blizzards and, in summer, mosquitoes. And, first and foremost, the glaciers, adding a spice of sensation and adventure to the whole. The Copper River runs at the foot of some of the largest glaciers in the world.

In one place, the engineers even ventured to lay the line over the glacier itself. To be able to take this risk, it was first necessary to make sure that the glacier was really 'dead'—no longer in motion. Glaciers are, after all, really rivers of ice, flowing sluggishly as a viscous mass, along a river bed. Some glaciers, however, such as the Allan Glacier along the Copper River, have not moved within man's memory.

Even though the Norwegian Southern Railway borrowed rotary snow ploughs from the Bergen Railway in the heavy snows of the 1950–51 winter, it could not do without its old and trusty aides—the pick and shovel brigades, who had plenty to do, as may be seen. We obtain our snow free, but have to pay to get rid of it. With a meticulous accuracy, that sets us all a good example, the State Railways reported that snow clearance that winter cost them exactly 10,898,697.76 kroner.

A railway bridge over the Copper River, Alaska. In the background is the Child Glacier, which many times threatened to destroy the construction works. A part of the glacier has 'calved' and sent ice floes down the river, representing a continual menace to the bridge.

Here, therefore, the risk was taken of laying the railway line over the glacier-ice itself for a distance of five miles.

Such a dead glacier looks like anything but a river of ice. A layer of sand and earth covers the surface, but there is no means of telling whether or when the ice beneath may start to life again and resume its flow towards the sea. Should this happen to the Allan Glacier, that particular stretch of line will be out of action; the 'permanent way' will become impermanent and slide into the river. Hitherto, however, there have been no signs of any trouble for this daring bit of engineering.

Not all the glaciers along the Copper River are 'dead', however. One of the 'live' ones is Child Glacier. This rises from the bank of the river as a mighty ice cliff, nearly 500 feet high. The length of its steep face is over three miles. During the summer, the glacier 'calves' continuously along this whole front, and moves forward as much as ten feet in a day. No railway line built on such a glacier would still be there the following year. Even the boldest engineers quailed here, and preferred a bridge along the glacier face, but at a safe distance from it.

Bridge building at thirty to forty degrees below zero and in driving snow is no pleasure. The ice-bound river, though, was a help since it afforded a firm foothold everywhere. The bridge spans were supported on piers of heavy piling. These had to be rammed through six feet of ice. The usual ice-saws were useless in such conditions, but steam-jets supplied the answer: as the jets played on the ice, the piles sank in. And the steam held the piles free from the grip of the ice until they were firmly rammed in the river bottom. When the piles had been placed, the whole was allowed to freeze over again. Suddenly, however, a burst of spring weather set in. It thawed when it should have frozen hard. Rainwater covered the ice two feet deep. The glacier woke from its winter sleep, and moved down on the bridge. Owing to ice-blocks further down, the rising water lifted the ice-shield on the river, and a terrible catastrophe seemed indeed imminent.

All the piles were frozen in the ice and the bridge girders were already in place. When the piles began to move with the ice it appeared as if the whole structure would collapse. All construction work was stopped and the whole labour force turned to meet the new menace. Soon, the ice began to rise again, and the bridge structure began to crack and give way. Then the steam-jets were again set in action. The ice was forced to loose its grip on the piles, which fell back into their places, clashing and groaning. At the same time, men worked madly on the bridge girders to make good the damage and force everything back into place. Gradually gaining experience in this unaccustomed work the railway builders managed to hold the danger in check. Then, however, the neighbouring glaciers themselves started to move. They discharged large blocks of ice into the river above the bridge. The pressure of the rising water became too great, burst the ice-shield over the river and hurled the pieces against the trestles supporting the bridge. In some places the piles broke like matchsticks, and collapse seemed imminent. Then the Child Glacier moved forward to its final attack. It began to 'calve', and a torrent of ice blocks and bergs mingled

This 'suspension' bridge was not meant as such; a flood washed the embankment away. It happened in Switzerland, but has been known to happen elsewhere; and in the tropics, torrential rains often produce such wash-outs.

with the pack ice above the bridge. The bridge appeared doomed, but the builders and their men did not flinch, repairing the damage as fast as it was caused. At last the ice below the bridge broke up, and the ice pack and icebergs floated down. The forces of winter ceased their attack and the bridge was saved.

A railway is in essence a work of mechanical regularity. It is not merely a chance assembly of rails, trucks, engines and structures, but a connected, organized whole. This system, this machinery, must run like clockwork. It is not enough that trains can run from London to Glasgow, from Paris to Rome, at a speed and with a degree of comfort never before equalled or dreamed of. A railway must do, must be capable of, far more. Not only must I be able to travel from London to Paris in a comfortable carriage, but I must be able to do this every day and know that I can leave London at say, 10 a.m., and be in Paris that same evening, at say, 7 p.m. And I know that all that the railway authorities can do will be done to make sure that these times are held to the minute. The difference between the railway and other forms of transport is just this almost absurdly punctilious insistence on minutes in the time-table. The train leaves at 3.21, and arrives at 10.23. That is no pretence, no advertising stunt; that is day-to-day reality. To maintain this strict timing is the aim and the pride of a railway. The standard may not always be reached or maintained, but the standard is there!

A network of railways now covers the world, from tropical swamps to the eternal snows. All have one aim in view—maximum punctuality with maximum safety. Even the layman will appreciate the magnitude of this goal. The natural obstacles and dangers encountered in operation may be so great that second thoughts may arise as to the construction of a railway on account of the operating difficulties which may follow. This was what very nearly happened with the Bergen Railway in Norway, which, it was considered, would be impossible to operate on account of snow-falls.

In the first few years of this railway it did seem as if the pessimists had been right, and that the great effort made in the construction of the line had been wasted. The obstacles to be overcome by the operating staff are often as great as those encountered by the original builders. This conflict with the forces of Nature is unceasing, it continues day by day, all the year round. The railway must always be ready to go out and meet the enemy—whether in pitched battle, or in isolated skirmishes. The foes of the railway are animal, vegetable and mineral— stifling heat and icy cold, devastating floods and searing drought, land slides, rock falls, snow blocks. Against these man pits all his experience, all his scientific and technical knowledge of the complicated interplay of natural forces, and his high capacity for patiently and systematically observing and descrying Nature's secrets. Vast, enduring forces are involved, both terrible and seemingly capricious in their actions. They are not so incalculable, however, as many think. They tend to repeat themselves, and this is where the patiently-observing engineer steps in.

After a few attacks, Nature no longer finds him unprepared. Measures have been taken and defences erected against the next visitation. Here and there, the natural forces still score a victory, still succeed in stopping a train, still bring death and devastation. They may cause annoyance to travellers by delays, but nowhere have they been allowed to triumph finally over Man's ultimate, obstinate defence. On the contrary, rail travel becomes safer and safer all over the world.

To appreciate the extent of the maintenance work daily necessary on the railways of the world let us just imagine what would happen if all this work were neglected. After a very short time all plant and structures would have become useless. When the Americans took over from the French the construction of the Panama Canal, they discovered

There would seem to be tunnels enough in any mountainous country, without building artificial ones. Such expensive works are, however, often the only safeguard against avalanches and rockfalls. Instead of building up such artificial head-cover, however, it is often possible to tunnel into the mountain side, even if the chosen alignment does not otherwise require this.

what happens when such man-made works are abandoned to the powers of the tropical jungle. The railways the French had built not half a generation before had in many places disappeared so completely that not even the 'trace' could be found. The warm, moist tropical air had in many places actually rusted away the rails. Little remained, either, of the 'permanent' way. The formation had been washed out, the cuttings had collapsed. Giant trees had grown over all, thick and flourishing as though Man had never set foot in these parts. The rolling stock, locomotives and wagons had also rusted and decayed away. The whole was so completely smothered in bush, creepers and lush vegetation as to defy all attempts to bring it to light. The Americans resolutely burnt off the jungle, and found only a graveyard dump of rusty relics.

This might not happen everywhere, but the forces of destruction are still continuously in action all over the world. In desert tracts, in a matter of days, a sandstorm may change even the whole landscape, cover the permanent way yards deep in sand, or sweep the whole track away. Rushing water has a distressing capacity for carrying everything away in its path. And in Norway, for instance, burrowing rodents are another problem. Every spring, the Railway Administration send out gangs to repair the ravages of the 'teledu', or stinking badger, in the earth of the formation. Sleepers lie crooked, rails have shifted; all needs overhauling, straightening and setting in place again. In mountainous country, rock-falls are the principal threat: stone slips which hurl large blocks on to the rails, and massive slides which may block the line for days.

Even such an apparently harmless phenomenon as sunshine on the rails may be the cause of tiresome stoppages. The heat of the sun has brought about many derailments, and caused loss of life. The tracks are laid with 50–60 foot lengths of rail, joined by fish-plates and bolts. On most modern lines intended for express traffic a number of rails are usually welded together in lengths of 200 feet and more, in order to reduce the number of shocks at the rail joints. Steel rails expand with heat and contract with cold; consequently, if there is insufficient space or play left between the rail butts, the track will twist and distort in the heat of the sun; it warps.

Even though, in our temperate climates, we cannot boast of such luxuriant vegetation as in the tropics, there is still work enough on the railways to keep the weeds away. Close and heavy traffic helps to

Even in the South American jungle, where man and horse find progress difficult, the railway makes its way.

G

suppress their growth, but if train intervals are long, conditions become more difficult. Any little used or deserted branch or siding will show this. The rails lie red with rust, nearly hidden in peaceful greenery. It all looks dead, and so different from the stripped efficiency of the traffic-polished rails and the clean, tidy ballast-surface of the main lines.

The troubles which many early reactionaries hoped would arise from cattle on the line have generally failed to materialize. But it did once happen on a French railway that a single cow derailed an express train, with loss of many lives. Fences on both sides of the line are necessary—a most expensive item. On the Narvik Railway there are no such fences, and occasionally a train does run into a herd of reindeer. The effect is devastating: not for the train, which suffers hardly at all, but for the animals. Fortunately, it does not happen often, but no reliable means of preventing such accidents has yet been found. On the North American prairies, in former days, even more exciting adventures could be experienced: a large herd of bison, the American buffalo, might cross the line. Even the driver of a powerful locomotive would hesitate to interfere with them, and even the express trains had to wait.

These are, however, all isolated instances which have done little harm to railway traffic. Even India's elephants have never banded themselves together to offer organized opposition to the railway, although in sufficient numbers they could turn an engine-driver's hair white with anxiety.

The smaller representatives of the animal world have proved much

Snowstorms, avalanches, floods and rock-falls are not the only dangers that railways have to contend with. In countries bordering sandy deserts miles of railway track may be buried in a few hours by sandstorms like that illustrated here. Such countries build few railways.

It would seem highly presumptuous for grasshoppers to attempt to stop a train; but unity and self-sacrifice work wonders. It is a gruesome sight when the locomotive churns through these masses of insects. Even when ground to pulp, the grasshoppers can still stop the train when the wheels cease to grip on the slimy rails. The line is being swept clean, in the path of the train.

more troublesome. In South America, for instance, grasshoppers—or rather, locusts—have often proved a menace. If a train runs into a thick swarm of these insects they are mown down and crushed in their thousands and millions, but the victory is short-lived. In death, they triumph; their crushed carcasses cover the rails with such a thick, slimy pulp, that the engine wheels spin uselessly, and the train can advance no further. The surviving locusts finally swarm over the whole engine, choking all moving parts, and the train has to stop and wait until the swarm passes on. Cleaning a locomotive after such a visitation is no easy task.

The most bitter struggle to keep the line free is to be witnessed, however, in the high mountains, among the everlasting snows. Those who have fought their way forward through a snow blizzard know the feeling of helplessness in the grip of overwhelming forces. It is no longer necessary for the ordinary man to expose himself to these dangers, however. Any reasonably sound sleeper can turn out, fresh and fit, to breakfast in the restaurant-car of the Oslo-Bergen night express without any idea or recollection of how the train fought its way through 'the worst storm of the century' during the night.

Snow attacks railways in cold climates in three different ways. The snowfall may be so heavy that all traffic is completely blocked, even in calm weather. It may be annoying to be held up at a wayside station by snow, facing glowing placards with invitations to a tour of the Riviera, but it is not dangerous. The other form of attack, the snow-storm or blizzard, is far more serious. In a few minutes it can whip up enormous snowdrifts which block the lines finally and completely. At the same time, the storm makes the work of the rescue parties almost impossible. Finally, the third form of attack is the snowslide or ava-lanche, which makes a concentrated thrust on a narrow front. As is well-known, avalanches can be a real danger to individual trains, and also a menace to traffic generally.

On the Ofoten Railway in Norway whole trains have been derailed and hurled down the mountain-side; this is not to be wondered at, since such avalanches can be of enormous size. Observations on a Canadian railway in the high mountains showed that an avalanche travelled over a steep slope nearly half a mile long, in just half a minute; the front of this avalanche was 1,000 feet wide, and the total mass of snow involved was calculated at 1,000,000 tons. The impact energy of such a mass, moving at the rate of a mile a minute, can well be imagined! It corre-sponds, roughly, to 3,000 express locomotives, charging forward in line abreast at 60 m.p.h.—an irresistible shock. Even smaller avalanches develop tremendous force, and it has proved best to avoid those stretches of country which are particularly exposed to this danger. If this is not easy, various subterfuges are adopted, to evade or hide from the enemy. No reasonable railway engineer has ambitions to try conclusions with an avalanche; he desires only to carry the line across the dangerous area as safely as possible.

When building up avalanche defences, the aim is not to block and stop the fall, but to deflect the mass of snow from the line, to prevent harm. In the Alps, much use is made of stone walls on the upper slopes, set at an angle to the prevailing direction of the avalanches to guide the fall harmlessly down into the valley. More often than not, however, the simplest and safest remedy is to put the line under cover—to hide from the avalanche. A structure of beams and planks forms an artificial tunnel or 'snow shed' on which the avalanche can fall and slide over the train into the valley below. It is, however, so expensive to build these snow-sheds, and particularly to keep them in good repair, that it is often cheaper to build a real tunnel.

Avalanches are a sufficiently grave menace, but they are, essentially, localized dangers, restricted in time and place. It is not difficult to observe their ways and to devise means of evading or deflecting them. The snow storm or blizzard must be placed in quite a different category. It sweeps over hundreds of square miles of the mountain slopes, bring-ing wild confusion in its train. The thin, black line of the railway,

This shows how even a long and heavy, iron-ore train on the Ofoten Railway to Narvik can be torn and tossed like a plaything, by a full-grown blizzard. The snow masses rushed down the mountain side and carried the whole train with them, with the result shown.

stretching over the high slopes, appears infinitely small and humble, even on a bright, fine day. When the blizzard begins and the smooth slopes are transformed into bellowing confusion, when all shape and outline are lost in the flurrying snow clouds, the railway, proud work of man's hands, no longer forms the centre of the scene. Even the giant mountain locomotives, the imposing, long rows of carriages, so large and important as they come rolling into the station covered in ice and snow, appear small and insignificant as they battle their way in the darkness across the mountains: puny dwarfs, mere playthings in the grip of the storm, daring its power and its fury.

What is six-foot man with his fragments of steel and metal compared with the mighty giant who has ruled on the fells these thousands of years? Little, puny man has been a bold challenger, however; he has met and fought the blizzard on its own ground among the mountain snows, has accepted all the risks. There are no rules in this game, no referee to see fair play—but in the end, man has won. He has proudly dared the storm, faced the toils and perils of the high slopes, accomplished the seemingly hopeless task. Mere men have done this, all in their day's work, throughout the changing seasons year by year; they have continued the fight against storm, blizzard and landslide. The trains go through!

The railwaymen conduct their campaign against snow and tempest with patience and prudence. They can give away no chances. There is no permanent cure for a blizzard. A waterfall can be damned, diverted, imprisoned in pipes, restrained and mastered in many ways. The wind bloweth where it listeth, and there is no way of controlling it. It must be met, prudently, patiently, with no rash gestures. Its whims and its ways must be studied. Cool calculation and skilful foresight must be used, the moods and vagaries of storms and blizzards learned, their causes and beginnings brought to light, their action and effect measured. Figures are determined—actual measurements arranged in long, prosaic tables showing the distribution and variation of wind-force, of wind direction and duration, of snowfall and temperature, of the paths of the snow masses, and all the essential features of the blizzards.

There is a touch of humour in reflecting how the forces of Nature have been restrained and combated with the help of these columns of figures on scraps of paper. There is no touch of humour in the prosaic results, however: they show what amazingly simple means suffice to counter the fury of the elements. This capacity of mankind for observation, consideration, evaluation and deduction from facts to the right answers has been the most valuable weapon in the conquest of Nature. Without this faculty, indeed, there would be little difference in mental equipment between man and a performing dog.

In this way, and by such means, the secret ways of storms have gradually been unravelled. For example, we now command a store of information about 'prevailing winds', for the storm has not only moods and caprices, it has also very firmly fixed habits; and an enemy with fixed habits is much more easily subdued. This information enables us to ascertain the places where the wind tends to lay the snow in large drifts, while sweeping other places clear. This is valuable knowledge and good use is made of it.

Thus equipped, we can first of all give our railway a suitable alignment, in so far as we have freedom of choice in the matter. Second, we can take steps to protect it from natural dangers, for though we cannot effectively alter the face of the winter landscape in the high

Two types of snow plough used by British Railways. The top picture shows a London Midland Region locomotive equipped with a small plough. Below is a giant snow plough of the North Eastern Region, used on the stretch of line which crosses the Pennines between Darlington and Tebay, where some of the worst falls and drifts of snow occur. These giant ploughs are 12 feet high and weigh 20 tons. They are operated by two heavy goods engines, and are able to deal with drifts up to 15 feet deep.

mountains, we can pay special attention to certain specific danger spots on the line. Whether drifts form in the one spot or in another fifty or a hundred yards away may make all the difference to a railway, and to passengers wanting to make their steamer connexions at the end of the line.

The permanent fortifications in the battle of the blizzards are of two kinds—snow-fences, and snow-sheds. The former are board fences of varying height, set obliquely, at some distance from the line. They are usually arranged in long rows. Their effect is to deflect the snow masses which come drifting over before the wind, and guide them away from the line. There is no intention of holding up the snow in large drifts, as many people think, and thus keeping it away from the line. It would be quite hopeless to attempt this; the masses of snow involved are far too great. The intention is to cause the drifts to form somewhere else—at a safe distance from the line.

At the start, small, low fences are tried in a variety of different positions. The final fences may be some 14–20 feet high. The correct positioning of these snow-fences is a very difficult problem, and involves many considerations. Unpleasant surprises may be encountered. After the screens have been in place for some time, and have proved satisfactory, a snow storm may blow up one day from an unexpected direction, perhaps directly against the prevailing wind. The screens then

Snow fences are not intended to stop the snow; on the contrary, they deflect the snow from the railway line, force it to form its drifts elsewhere. There is a great art in setting snow fences correctly. This view is near Myrdal, Norway, on the Bergen-Oslo line.

In countries like Norway, there are many parts of the railway line where neither snow ploughs nor snow fences can help. The line is then run in an artificial tunnel. In summer, these snow sheds may seem purposeless and irritating; but when the winter snows set in, their drawbacks are forgotten and their protection is welcome.

act in an exactly opposite way to that intended. Instead of diverting the snowdrifts away from the line they cause them to build up at that very point. This is why snow-screens, however effective they may be and however well they have served generally, are always considered a somewhat dubious form of protection. They are used only where the prevailing winds invariably do prevail.

There are other points to consider. The direction of the prevailing wind should as far as possible be *along* the line. If the wind as a rule blows across the line, snow-screens will be of no use; they will in fact more often be harmful, since they will tend to deflect the snow straight on to the line. In such places, snow-sheds are preferred. From the tourist passenger's standpoint, snow-sheds are an unpopular form of protection: they do keep the snow off in winter, but they also keep out the view, both in winter and summer. Nor do the railway engineers like them, for they are rather expensive and not so easy to build as might be imagined; above all, they are very expensive to keep in good repair. Without proper inspection and maintenance they can be a real danger to traffic. Some years ago, a loose plank fell on to a train and crashed through a railway carriage compartment—fortunately without loss of life.

Snow-sheds have to withstand both snow-pressure and wind-pressure. In snow storms, the heavy white snow-drifts, piled yards high over the shed, can break down the strongest wooden structure. To mitigate the wind pressure and at the same time allow light and air into the shed, it is kept open on the lee side—that is, the side away from the wind. Otherwise, there is a strong suction effect on this side, and pressure may build up within the shed, strong enough to burst the walls open. The greatest enemies of the snow-sheds are, however, sun and wind, which dry out, shrink and warp the wooden structure and weaken it to the point of danger.

Even if these 'fortifications' of the railway were fully efficient, the snow would speedily conquer if we had not also 'mobile defences', of which the snow plough represents the heavy artillery and pick-and-shovel the small arms. Ordinary snow ploughs, which merely push the snow aside, are of two kinds. The smaller type is simply fitted on the front of a locomotive, and is able to keep the line clear during ordinary snowfalls in the lowlands. Where the snowfalls are heavier the larger plough is used. This is nearly as high and wide as a railway truck, but otherwise of the characteristic plough shape. Such ploughs are preferably worked by special, snow-clearing trains, powered by several locomotives.

Neither of these ploughs, however, can cope with the tremendous snowdrifts raised by storms in the high mountains. There, heavier equipment is necessary. The best solution hitherto found is the *rotary snow plough*, first invented by Leslie in America, in the 1880's. The type used on the Bergen Railway is a fairly large railway truck carrying a locomotive boiler and a powerful steam engine, usually of about 800 h.p. This engine does not, as in a railway locomotive, drive the wheels, but it turns a horizontal shaft running lengthwise along the truck and carrying in front a large wheel or 'fan' about ten feet in diameter. The vanes or scoops of the fan have sharp steel cutting-edges, which dig into the snow and force it back into conical scoops. These are open at the circumference of the wheel, which is, however, completely

A rotary snow plough in action. Without the 'rotaries' it would be almost hopeless to try to keep the Norwegian railways operating in winter on the mountains and in other exposed places. The Bergen Railway now has four such rotary ploughs, stationed between Al and Voss; and there are three on the Nordland line. These ploughs have 600 h.p. steam-engines to drive the rotaries, but only one of 1,300 h.p. is self-propelled. Otherwise, one or two locomotives are used to push the plough. These 120-ton giants cut through even the largest drifts at a speed of not less than 4 miles an hour.

surrounded by a cylindrical casing except at the top. When the scoops successively arrive beneath this opening the snow is thrown out in a tremendous jet.

The rotary snow plough is pushed by one or more locomotives. When it gets started along the line, it takes something to stop it. In deep and dense snowdrifts, of course, progress is slower—but just as sure. In loose snow, of not too great depth, the plough advances at about the speed of a slow goods train.

Not so very long ago trains did not venture to travel at night, even in the most peaceful country. Now, passengers sleep peacefully while the train rushes over the wild mountains in storm and snow. This is one of the triumphs of engineering. What was once a fantastic dream has become a daily occurrence, and that not merely by inventiveness and superior science. The greatest part has been played by the continual attention, the daily care, the unwearying reliability, of honest, hard maintenance work—in fact, by all that is known as 'service'. The passenger sees only the results: the trains arrive at their destinations safely and punctually, the carriages are clean and comfortable and reasonably warm, the reading-lamps over the berths are well placed and in good working order. The sum total of planning, ideas, conscientiousness, toil and trouble, which has been necessary to ensure the ticket-holding passengers' comfort and safety through winter nights and mountain tempests, is too little realized, too often forgotten.

CHAPTER IV

GIANTS OF THE IRON ROAD

A TECHNICAL problem is not a mathematical equation; it cannot be solved by formulae and calculation alone: it is always necessary to satisfy a number of frequently conflicting conditions. It is, therefore, impossible to predict everything. Few technical problems give such a clear example of this as the design of a locomotive. The many requirements to be considered in the design of a modern railway engine, and the many conflicting conditions to be fulfilled, easily prove that a locomotive represents one of the most imposing expressions of engineering skill.

The outstanding feature of all modern locomotive design is the way in which power and tractive force have been pressed into the smallest possible space. The whole, enormous mechanism must be squeezed into the limits of the 'loading gauge', the free space available in tunnels, and under bridges. This requirement is imperative and allows of no deviations. The only unrestricted dimension is *length*; and even there the designer is fettered. A long and *rigid* locomotive will not be able to pass the curves on the line; it can, however, be *articulated*, or jointed, and thus enabled to 'snake' its path through the curves of the permanent way. The Garratt locomotive of this type is said to be limited only by the distance between stations!

The *weight* must be both the least and the greatest permissible. The weight on each wheel must be as small as required by the strength of the rails and the bridges over which the locomotive runs. The weight, on the driving wheels on the other hand, must be as large as possible, to obtain the maximum adhesion: a locomotive cannot pull a train with a greater force than about one-quarter of its own adhesion weight. If this force is exceeded, the driving wheels slip.

The force we describe as friction is usually regarded as something of an enemy. Quite rightly: the amount of energy expended year by

Wheels are being fitted to a locomotive—or, rather, the engine is being put on wheels.

year in overcoming friction in all the world's machinery must be tremendous. It is encountered everywhere, and the abolition of friction would represent a true revolution in the life of the world.

The railway folk, however, do not look upon friction as their worst enemy. On the contrary, to them friction is somewhat more important than the managing director: they could do without *him*, but not without friction, which enables them to drive their engines and draw their trains.

The force exerted by the driving wheels of a locomotive on the rails, *i.e.*, its tractive force, is easily determined. The so-called co-efficient of friction between the wheels and the rails is about 0·25, or

A machine for balancing locomotive driving-wheels. The nearest wheel carries a 'balance weight' on top. Below, is the crank-pin for the connecting and coupling-rod pins. In the test, this pin is loaded with the same weight as will have to be carried on the locomotive. The whole must now be balanced, so that the wheels do not 'pound' when rotated.

one-quarter. If we multiply this by the *proportion of the locomotive weight resting on the driving wheels*, the so-called 'adhesion weight', we get the tractive force. Thus, if the friction is nil, the tractive force is also zero. We could then use railway carriages to help the housing shortage, but for no other purpose.

Large railway locomotives have a few more wheels, in addition to the driving wheels proper. Only a part of the total weight is used for adhesion. If, on the U.S.A. railways, an axle load of thirty tons is allowed, then, a locomotive with eight pairs of driving wheels (eight on each side), will have an adhesion weight of 240 tons, and, given sufficient steam pressure and cylinder volume, might give a tractive force of one-quarter of that amount, or sixty tons. The locomotive itself will probably weigh well over 240 tons; more powerful but lighter locomotives will not be possible in this world, until we can obtain tractive force by means other than the friction between the wheel and the rail.

It will thus be seen that there are certain limitations imposed on the locomotive designer and builder. On the other hand, the requirements made often seem to surpass all bounds. Railway managers continue to demand bigger and better locomotives with higher and higher speeds, and greater and greater tractive-effort. How to achieve this is left entirely to the designer. He, poor man, is usually also limited in his

A Beyer-Garratt locomotive coaling. Modern coal bunkers have considerably simplified this operation.

scope. He cannot choose an electric locomotive for a steam railway, nor use oil or pulverized coal firing if the locomotives are expected to run on coal of a particular type from the railway's own mines. As a matter of fact, some fifty years ago there was *no* choice in this matter. All railways of any importance, all over the world, used only *one* kind of locomotive engine—the coal-fired, reciprocating-engine, the direct descendant of Stephenson's *Rocket*. As in many other branches of engineering, the course of years has brought with it many new possibilities, many new solutions. The old, piston-driven steam locomotive has itself developed new forms. Superheating, multiple cylinders, bogie trucks, high-pressure boilers, feed-water heaters, and many other features have been introduced, which in course of time have considerably improved the efficiency of the steam locomotive. Furthermore, entirely

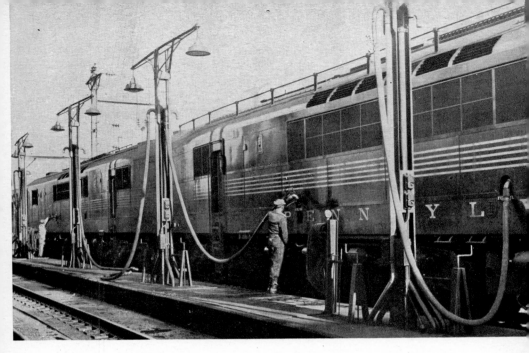

Compared with diesel locomotives sucking up their liquid fuel, even the best means of loading coal appear cumbersome.

new locomotive types have appeared: turbine locomotives, with and without condensers, electric locomotives, combined diesel-electric locomotives, and, finally, what many railway engineers consider the type of the future—the gas-turbine locomotive.

An amusing novelty, which represented a radical break with the traditional principles of locomotive engineering, was the 'rail-borne Zeppelin' of the 1920's, now but a memory. This dispensed with everything dispensable, including driving wheels, and rolled along the railway tracks, driven or drawn by an airscrew. This locomotive was, consequently, independent of friction between wheel and rail, and did not require weight for power.

There is something homely and cosy about a railway locomotive. We need not wrinkle our brows to 'see how it works'. There is a fire inside the boiler, and that produces steam which drives the pistons to and fro in the cylinders. The latter are to be seen, at the side, under the boiler and in front of the driving wheels; and there are also the piston-rods, which work in and out of the cylinders and drive the cross-heads to and fro in their well-oiled guides, the connecting rods from the crossheads to the crank-pins on one pair of wheels, and the coupling-rods connecting all the driving wheels together.

However simple this old locomotive, in the Steam Age it repre-

The little 'kettle' was an engineering wonder in its day—round about 1861 though consider-ably smaller than the giants of our day. The very large Pennsylvania locomotive in the background was an experiment, and did not actually enter service.

sented the first piece of machinery that boys could plainly understand and patiently explain to their elders. Even in the present age, when so many technical wonders compete for our attention, many of us are still drawn to the old steam locomotive, with its very simple mechanism driven by truly titanic forces. True enough, and simple enough, in the parts exposed to our view. But on taking one of our modern loco-motives to pieces we shall find enough of interest to think over! Obviously, a machine which for the last century has carried the bulk of the world's land transport must incorporate an exceptional amount of inventive faculty and scientific research. It is an object worth study-ing, since any improvement can effect a material, economic gain.

The steam locomotive remains the same, in its essential principles, as it was a century and more ago. These principles set automatic limits to its development, but within such limits technical refinements have carried its performance as far as is possible. Hence, a modern locomotive burns only about half the quantity of coal required by its predecessors some forty years ago, and the modern locomotive develops about double the power per pound of steam generated. At the beginning of this century it was somewhat of a feat to develop 1,200 h.p. on ten coupled wheels. Now, there are locomotives which develop as much power on each pair of wheels.

It is not, essentially, very difficult to burn coal and make steam. When it is a question of a modern locomotive, however, which may burn as much as twelve tons of coal *per hour*, it becomes something of a problem both to feed such a quantity of coal to the furnace, and to enable it to burn properly at such a rate. There is no room, even on a giant locomotive, for a whole gang of stokers or firemen on the footplate. The enormous consumption of coal calls for a 'mechanical stoker', which may, for instance, consist of an endless screw or worm, which presses the coal forward from the tender to the firebox. Coal broken small is needed, in order to facilitate this movement.

Twelve tons of coal per hour cannot be burnt in a single furnace without forcing the draught. One cannot put a factory chimney on a locomotive. On the contrary, as our pictures show, the 'chimney' shrinks as the locomotive swells. The little steam kettle of older days shown on page 114 carried a mighty 'stack' for a chimney. It would be difficult to find any such stack on the panting giant in the background, which has grown so big as to fill the whole loading gauge.

The draught in a tall chimney stack appears to us quite 'natural'. But in the steam locomotive the necessary draught is obtained by passing the expanded steam from the cylinders, after it has done its work, up through a 'blast-pipe' with a narrowed top to the chimney. In this way a strong suction effect is produced, providing draught for the fire. So there is something in that comfortable panting, in time with the piston beats, which characterizes the 'puff-puff' train of our childhood.

It is unnecessary and uninteresting for the general reader to go too deeply into all the details and refinements to be found in a modern railway locomotive. That there are enough of them for a lifetime's study, and that they are sufficient to occupy the full attention of the driver, will be to some extent plain from the picture on p. 127, which shows some of the instruments in the driver's cab of a modern, steam locomotive. We could well spare a thought for the driver, who has stood through the dark night behind all these gauges, levers and handwheels when we leave our comfortable sleepers!

Instead of floundering in details we will content ourselves with

Ordinary locomotives have 'fire-tube' boilers, the furnace-gases passing through tubes immersed in the water. This high-pressure engine, built by the L.N.E.R., was fitted with a 'water-tube' (marine-type) boiler, in which the water circulated through tubes surrounded by the furnace-gases. It was not a success, and has been rebuilt on ordinary lines.

taking a look at the main features of a locomotive's anatomy. If we count the wheels on each side of a powerful locomotive such as the *Texas Flash*, illustrated below, we find first two small wheels in front, then three wheels coupled together, and lastly one small wheel at the rear. We risk the assumption that there are as many wheels on the other side, and call the locomotive a '4–6–2' type. In this notation, the driving wheels are always represented by the figure in the middle; the leading wheels are on the left and the trailing wheels on the right.

Small locomotives such as 'shunters' or 'switchers' may have only four driving wheels, and no leading or trailing wheels. That is a 0–4–0 arrangement. Powerful, but not very speedy, locomotives may have up to 0–8–0 or 0–10–0. For higher speeds, the locomotive is given a 'leading' four-wheeled bogie-truck, to guide it round curves. This leads to the 4–6–0 or 4–8–0 wheel arrangement. To support the firebox of a larger locomotive, a two-wheel or four-wheel 'trailing truck' may be added, making the wheel arrangement 4–6–2 or 4–8–2, or 4–6–4 or 4–8–4.

The number of driving wheels is, as we have seen, dependent first on the adhesion weight to be carried, and second, on the weight per wheel or axle which the rails and the bridges on the line can support. In America, some lines allow an axle load up to 35 tons; fewer driving wheels are then necessary to carry a high adhesion weight and thus develop a high tractive force. If the permissible axle loading for the line is halved, the number of driving wheels must be doubled. For such cases, the Americans have built locomotives up to 4–12–2, *i.e.*, with no less than twelve driving wheels in a single, rigid wheelbase.

As will be appreciated, such a locomotive cannot 'snake' its way along sharp curves. Five pairs of coupled wheels are a fair length to

Texas Flash, a powerful, steam locomotive which ran between Kansas City and Dallas, Tex., with the beginnings of a fairing justifying the title of 'semi-streamlined'. In the locomotive classification, it belongs to the 4–6–2 type, with 4 leading wheels, 6 driving wheels, and 2 trailing wheels. This type has since been scrapped.

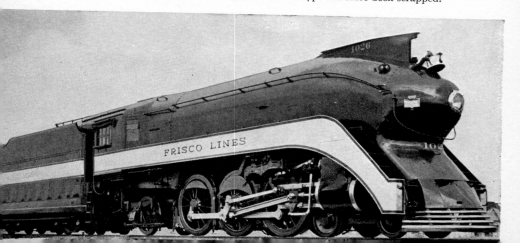

This Pennsylvania Railroad locomotive, one of the most powerful types ever built, could draw up to 125 fully-laden bogie freight wagons at a speed of 50 miles an hour.

drive along the rails. With the wheels thus clamped in a rigid frame it does not require much of a curve to make either the front or the rear wheels jump the rails, and drag the rest with them. If such long loco- motives are, therefore, required to run on lines with any fairly sharp curves, the driving wheels must be made independent of each other.

This is not the case with the locomotive shown above, however. Five of the ten driving wheels are visible: these are arranged in two sets—four in front and six behind, each set driven by its own two cylinders. Since there are now four driving wheels in front, and six behind them, the type is 4–4+6–4. Each of the two sets of driving wheels is mounted in the one set of main frames; the idea of this arrangement is to permit the division of the normal very large two cylinders into four, so permitting the use of smaller and lighter moving parts. The carrying wheels at front and rear are mounted in separate bogie trucks. The Pennsylvania Railroad built a number of similar 4–4–4–4 locomotives for express passenger service, but both these classes have now been scrapped in favour of diesel traction.

This line of development leads naturally to the wholly-articulated locomotive. Essentially, this consists of two separate locomotives each with its own steam machinery, driving and carrying wheels, but both taking steam from the same boiler. In the one type, invented by the Frenchman, *Anatole Mallet*, and called after him, the driver's cab, firebox and boiler are built on to the rear of one of the two engine frames. The boiler projects over the front frame (which is, of course, pivoted to the rear frame). The boiler is supported with its front end

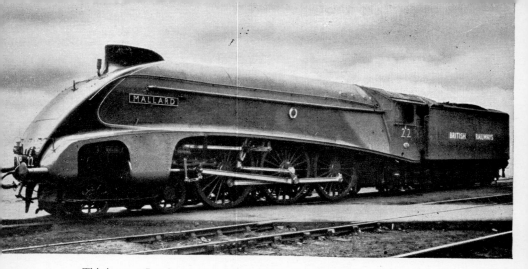

This is an ex-London & North Eastern locomotive of the Class 'A4' 4–6–2 type, the famous *Mallard*, leader in the top class of 'streamliners'. This masterpiece of traditional British engineering skill has attained a maximum speed of 126 miles an hour, the highest ever reached by a steam locomotive.

sliding over the top of the front frame; in curves, therefore, the front frame with its cylinders, driving and carrying (leading) wheels, can swing sideways or pivot, under the projecting smokebox end of the boiler.

The most logical development of the 'jointed' (or 'articulated') steam locomotive is represented by the second type, invented by *H. W. Garratt*, and technically developed by the British firm of locomotive builders, Beyer, Peacock & Co., for which reason it is usually called the Beyer-Garratt locomotive. The construction in this case enables the locomotive designer to increase the length of the boiler to any extent he pleases. The outcome of this pleasing and symmetrical design is pictured on p. 119. This shows clearly the two separate driving units, one right in front, and one right behind. They act simultaneously as tenders. The driving cab and boiler are carried between these two driving trucks, on bridge girders. The weight of the boiler is thus transmitted to the driving trucks and increases the adhesion weight of the driving wheels. The small carrying wheels under the centre girder are part of the leading truck. The classification of the Beyer-Garratt locomotive shown is, therefore, 4–8–2 + 2–8–4.

With these two articulated types locomotive builders can achieve wonders in regard to weight and power. The largest steam locomotive in the world is claimed to be a 4–8–8–4 Mallet, of the Union Pacific Railroad, weighing with tender no less than 535 tons, and measuring more than 130 feet in length.

On well-designed, substantially-built, railway lines, these locomotives can profit by the high permissible wheel-loads to develop

An example of the powerful articulated locomotive type designed by *H. W. Garratt*, and developed by Beyer, Peacock & Co., the Manchester locomotive builders. The two sets of driving gear, each with 8 driving wheels, form two separate chassis, that in front carrying the water tank, and that in the rear the (oil) fuel tank and a second water tank. Between them is the oil-fired boiler common to the two, and the driving cab.

tremendous tractive power. There are other regions, also, in which they are found useful. On lines of lighter construction, and in particular as regards bridges where the wheel loads require to be light, these long Mallet locomotives with their many driving wheels spread their weight over a considerable length of track, and though the curves may be abrupt, they give no difficulty to an engine of the adaptable Beyer-Garratt type. Many locomotives of the latter kind are at work overseas.

Articulated locomotives are, however, unsuitable for very high speeds. The British railways have specialized in fast locomotives and have developed a number of top-ranking types, usually with the 4–6–2, or 'Pacific', or 4–6–0 wheel arrangement. Before nationalization, the London & North-Eastern Railway, which, among other trains, ran the *Coronation* streamliner between London and Edinburgh, introduced a class of particularly imposing locomotives. The creator was one of the most famous locomotive engine builders in the world, Sir Nigel Gresley, and the class, although 'A1' in essence, was a development called 'A4'. It includes some of the leading record-holders among steam locomotives, *e.g.*, *Mallard*, which has run at 126 m.p.h. Such locomotives are used on express services with booked timings which demand speeds up to 90 m.p.h.

A modern articulated steam locomotive of the Southern Pacific Railroad, U.S.A., which is of interest in that oil-firing permits the driver's cab to be at the leading end, and the chimney at the trailing end, with the 12-wheel tender following. The locomotive wheel arrangement is 4–8–8–2, with two groups of eight-coupled wheels. The leading chassis is integral with the main frame, and the trailing chassis is pivoted.

Over the principal British main lines the maximum permissible speed again is 90 m.p.h. At speeds of a mile a minute and more every extra mile represents added cost, especially in coal. To effect some saving, some locomotives are sheathed in a streamlined casing, lowering the air resistance. Streamlining in railway locomotives—unlike motor cars—is used only to ensure very high speeds. Up to about

In the years between the two World Wars, a 'New Look' was provided for many steam locomotives and trains, a vision of beauty in shining, bright metal. But while the trains still retain it, steam locomotives like this *Crusader* of the Reading Railroad, U.S.A., have been supplanted by diesels.

90 m.p.h., the resistance of the surrounding air can be overcome at the cost of some 100 h.p., but at higher speeds the air resistance rises disproportionately. As the full speeds of the pre-war British streamline trains have not as yet been restored, and as streamline casings interfere with maintenance by reducing the accessibility of working parts, the streamlining of the London Midland Region Pacifics has been removed, though the Eastern Region 'A4' Pacifics remain much as before. However, 100 m.p.h. is being prepared for as a normal maximum speed in the future, even in Great Britain.

The ordinary, coal-fired steam locomotive has already reached practical perfection. The best we see today is a technical performance beyond all praise; but it is beginning to be inadequate in the face of the enormous increase in traffic requirements. Poor old 'Puffing Billy' is ready to resign pride of place to others.

If an old-time locomotive designer, racking his brains to find room for all the different parts required—furnace, boiler, cylinders, coal,

Dovregubbe (Dovre Lad), Norway's premier locomotive class, which is used to work heavy trains over the 3,360 ft. summit at Hjerkinn, on the way from Oslo to Trondheim.

water, and much else in addition—had been told of a locomotive engine without firebox, water-tank or boiler, which did not gulp lumps of coal but swallowed liquid fuel, tanking-up during short stops at stations, and did not need 'firing-up' for many hours before starting out on its day's run, after his first unbelieving laughter had subsided he would have freely acknowledged that a machine of that kind would be worth the extra price, however high.

That was exactly what the English inventor Ackroyd Stuart made possible. The old, conventional elements of a prime mover were an arrangement for burning fuel, a boiler to produce steam, and finally, a cylinder in which steam could expand behind a piston and push it forward. The internal combustion engine of Lenoir, Otto and Benz dispensed with the fire and boiler, burning the fuel—oil or gas— directly within the cylinders. But the fuel had to be ignited, and various systems of electrical ignition to explode the fuel after it was compressed in the cylinders were invented. This meant further complication, and it was Ackroyd Stuart's idea to utilize the fact that the compression of a gas raises its temperature. Why not compress it so highly that it will fire itself?

Rudolf Diesel followed Ackroyd Stuart and developed this idea in Switzerland. He departed considerably from Stuart in the details of firing, and this type of engine became known as the 'Diesel'. Though it was later found necessary to return to Ackroyd Stuart's method, the name 'Diesel' has become permanently attached to the self-ignition type of internal combustion engine.

The principle of the diesel engine is this: air is drawn into the cylinder and compressed to some 30 times atmospheric pressure (427 lb./sq. in.), which raises it to a temperature of 700–1,000°. Fuel oil is then injected into the heated air, where it at once ignites, and the resulting expansion of the gaseous products of combustion forces the piston down the cylinder.

Engines of this kind have revolutionized locomotive construction. Tenders, fire-boxes and boilers have been swept away, but in view of the mass of equipment—multi-cylinder diesel engines, electric generators, motors, fuel tanks, steam-heating boilers and their tanks for supplying water—required in a modern Diesel-electric locomotive it has little saving in length and weight to show as compared with a steam locomotive of comparable power.

In due course, the 'professionals' became used to this new order of things. It is difficult to give up old and tried, traditional methods and means, and it was some time before the diesel engine was accepted into the old-established family of locomotives. But when once a start had been made it very rapidly gained favour. In the United States of America there were, in 1934, some 54,000 steam locomotives and 1 (one) diesel; by the end of 1955 no fewer than 24,635 diesel-electric units were in service, of every imaginable kind—express passenger freight, shunting and the very popular combined 'road-switchers'— and they were handling 88 per cent. of the passenger coach-miles, 85 per cent. of the freight ton-miles, and 91 per cent. of the locomotive hours in shunting yards. Thousands of steam locomotives had been scrapped, and a greater volume of traffic was being moved by far fewer locomotives. This comparison is highly significant. Even though the steam locomotive has improved with the years, these figures clearly show that the diesel locomotive is even more efficient.

Its superiority can be demonstrated even more directly. A steam locomotive running 125,000 miles per annum is performing reasonably well. Top figures in America are probably 50 per cent higher. When a locomotive runs right round the Equator once in every seven weeks, and continues to do so all the year round, very heavy wear and tear are inevitable, and long periods of recuperation in the 'sick bay' are necessary. Thus, performance averaged over, say, ten years, is considerably reduced. On the other hand, diesel locomotives (such as that on the *Zephyr* between Denver and Chicago) have circled the world 140 times in ten years. In other words, they have run a distance equal to that from London to Blackpool and back daily for 7,000 consecutive days. There is probably not a single steam locomotive in the world which could beat this performance.

The final assembly of a diesel-electric locomotive in the General Motors shops. The roof, superstructure and driver's cab are being lowered on to the frame, which already has the machinery in place. Behind, is another locomotive, nearly completed and soon to start out from the shops on its first run. Nine such locomotives leave these shops every day.

It is far easier to swallow oil, as the diesel engine does, than to swallow coal in the manner of the steam locomotive. In addition, the diesel engine makes far better use of its liquid fuel. With the same weight

This picture is of historical interest, since it shows the first diesel-electric generating plant to be built on the American Continent. The pioneers were the Canadian National Railways, and when the Canadian engineers made their first trial run in 1929, they proved that they had great hopes of the new locomotive—hopes which have subsequently been fully justified. Railway engineering now started a new epoch, during which the U.S.A. alone found itself increasing its locomotive 'stud' by 650 diesel locomotives yearly.

of fuel it runs four, even five times the distance of a steam locomotive. The above run, from London to Blackpool and back, could be made on one load of fuel in the tank without filling up anywhere *en route.* The diesel does not need a separate tender: there is room for the fuel-tanks on the engine itself.

The conventional steam locomotive does not only burn fuel; it also consumes water in amazing quantities. It *must* have water. A steam-operated line in arid country cannot, therefore, be longer than the distance which a steam locomotive can run, *there and back*, with one load of water in the tender. There is little purpose in running a train out into the Sahara Desert and back again, merely to consume some

70–80 tons of water, so the Sahara must content itself with camels and cars. The diesel locomotive, however, could easily cross the waterless desert, *e.g.*, from Timbuctoo in the French Sudan to Algiers on the Mediterranean. But in regions with cold winter climates diesels must be equipped with small automatically fired boilers for supplying steam-heat to passenger trains; and for these boilers water supplies are, of course, necessary. Again, however, the diesel can find room in its underframe to accommodate the required water tanks.

To conclude this account, one more important fact must be mentioned. There is no particular difficulty in putting several locomotives to pull a train when one is not enough. There is, therefore, nothing exceptional in three or four diesel locomotives drawing a train. What is sensational, however, is that four diesels, of 1,500 h.p. each, can be coupled to form a single unit of 6,000 h.p. *driven by one man.* (See picture at foot of page.) The train shown appears to be headed one locomotive and three carriages. This is not so—this is one locomotive formed of four coupled diesel units. What about the poor fellow who has to drive this locomotive procession? Look at him in the picture at the bottom of page 127—in a simply, but comfortably arranged driving compartment, with a good, leather-covered armchair seat.

Look now at the top of the same page! His mate in the steam locomotive has a number of other things to do, but even in modern steam locomotives padded seats are now provided in the cab, as a matter of course, for the driver and fireman, so that they may rest when their duties permit.

The railwayman, however, also finds disadvantages in this wonderful diesel engine; it is not all monotonous perfection. A diesel engine cannot simply be fitted on a locomotive frame. For one thing, it runs at too high a speed even for our present hurrying age. For example,

A modern American diesel-electric locomotive formed of four separate units, each of 1,500 horse-power. The 'reins' of the total of 6,000 horses are held in one pair of hands—one man only, in a comfortable seat behind the front windscreen, controls all this machinery. This is a later version of the train pictured on page 37.

Once upon a time, coals were carried in baskets from the mine. Later, trucks were pushed along wooden rails. Halfway through the eighteenth century, some thirty thousand men, women and children pushed the heavy coal trams from the Durham collieries to the banks of the River Tyne. The drawing shows this infernal toil in progress. Engineering science has liberated all those thousands from their animal toil, and has enabled one man in the pit to control an electric locomotive hauling fifty trucks laden with two hundred tons of coal.

the engine shaft turns at not less than 1,000 revolutions per minute, and can only run at about this speed—a little less, or a little more. If coupled directly to the driving wheels, it would result in a somewhat uncomfortable locomotive since it would have only one speed.

A better solution is to gear the engine running at its 1,000 r.p.m. to the driving wheels in such manner that these can run at any convenient, lower speeds. Mechanical gears of this kind are difficult to design, build and run. Hence, an electric power transmission, a generator driven by the diesel engine, and supplying current to electric driving motors, is preferred. These 'diesel-electric' locomotives are a peculiar solution: a diesel engine, big enough and strong enough to drive the locomotive, drives a dynamo, and that drives one or more electric motors, and these, at last, turn the wheels. This is certainly not as good a solution as an engine capable of driving straight on to the locomotive wheels, and increases the cost of a diesel locomotive far beyond that of its steam counterpart.

Instead of electricity, a hydraulic transmission gear can be used. A diesel engine drives a rotor with a ring of blades enclosed in an oil-tight casing. This acts as a centrifugal pump, pressing oil through a guide-ring into a turbine-wheel, which is itself fitted on a driving axle of the locomotive. There is thus an elastic coupling, without direct mechanical contact, between the driving and the driven parts. By regulating the oil flow and pressure, the transmission ratio of the hydraulic gear can be altered. For reversing, a duplicate set of blade rings can be provided.

It is, of course, possible to use mechanical gears with a diesel engine, as with any other engine (such as that of a motor car). The gear unit has to be much larger and more powerful than a car gearbox, but the use of pneumatic (compressed-air) controls makes an easy matter of the gear-changing. Such a gear, however, can only change the transmission ratio stepwise, and is used principally for small locomotives—e.g., the

The two pictures on this page should be regarded as one, since together they show us something of the ways of technical development. Above is the driver's cab of a steam locomotive. It is sufficiently complicated, even though the fire, which also needs attention, is not visible. Below we see one man in a comfortable seat controlling not merely one, but as many as three to four, diesel-electric locomotives.

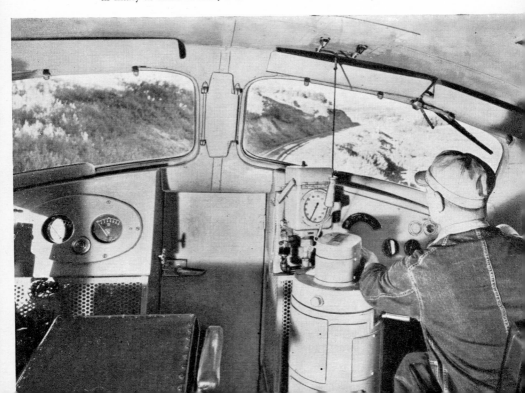

'diesel shunter'. The diesel-electric and diesel-hydraulic systems are, in effect, infinitely-variable gears.

In one respect, the steam locomotive is superior to the diesel, and can rightly claim to be more independent and self-contained. The diesel engine runs perfectly—when it is running; but, to be made to run, it has to start. The oil injected into the cylinder can only become ignited when the piston has compressed the air in the cylinder sufficiently to raise its temperature to the ignition point of the fuel. Then follows the 'combustion stroke' which gives the piston the impetus for its next stroke. With the engine at rest there is no compression, no ignition, and no force acting on the piston. Nothing happens, and the engine remains at rest. A steam engine, on the other hand, will start as soon as steam is admitted to the cylinder or cylinders.

Having paid our quarter of a million for a fine locomotive, we find it will not start of its own accord—no matter how well it will run when it has once been started. Here, we turn to the designer and builder and beg him to make our diesel locomotive start, somehow.

Small engines can be started by turning a handle, but we cannot resort to this with 2,000 h.p. In some cases we even call on the despised steam engine to help. In the 'steam-diesel' system, steam cylinders start the locomotive and the diesel engine takes over when running. Compressed air is also used but generally, in the case of locomotives the start is made electrically with current supplied by storage batteries, which are, in the case of diesel-mechanical (geared diesel drive) charged by a separate, small dynamo. In diesel-electric locomotives there is, of course, an electric plant already available to charge the starter batteries. Electric starting, even of the heaviest locomotives, is easier than with a family car. It is also extremely quick and reliable, and the driver can safely cut out engines when running downhill or when approaching a station.

In the competition between steam and diesel power, both types have been further and further improved and developed. Steam locomotives are equipped with superheaters, additionally heating the steam coming from the boiler, and some (notably French types) have poppet-valves instead of the more common piston valve and link or Walschaert's motion. In diesel engines, precompression of the air before entering the cylinders—the so-called supercharging or 'boosting'— has been introduced, and this has improved performance by 50 per cent.

The contest between the two rivals, however, is open and above board, and all the rules of the game are observed. Both are railway locomotives in the original sense of the word, i.e., a combination of prime mover and driving mechanism, running on its own wheels, hauling its loads by independent power. There is now a third competitor, which has gained some considerable advantage by breaking all the old rules. This unsporting rival is the electric locomotive.

This newcomer is something of a deceiver. It may well claim to be far, far more powerful than a 6,000 h.p. diesel, but, to put it quite bluntly, it is merely an empty shell. There is as much power in a bicycle as in these opulent, electrical heavyweights. They have no power of their own at all. It is a mere, empty boast, to call it a super-power locomotive; all it has are electric motors which can do the work of many thousands of horses—*when power is supplied to them from outside.*

This is the simple answer. We have our power stations all over the country, generating as much power as possible from coal and waterfalls,

An electrically-driven engine controlled by one (seated) driver, pulling a train of fifty trucks loaded with 200 tons of coal in a modern mine. This picture shows how engineering science has liberated thousands of labourers from such animal toil as that illustrated in the drawing at the top of page 126.

and sending it through a grid of power cables, from which our electric
'locomotive' can pick it up by putting out a pole to contact overhead
wires or lowering a 'shoe' to a live rail. Not surprisingly, therefore,
the steam and diesel locomotive fans claim that the electric locomotive
should be 'disqualified'—not for breaking the rules of the race, but
for not being a racer at all! Unlike the other giants of the iron road
it has no heart, no lungs, no hungry belly, and only receives power into
its blood and muscles from some mysterious, outside source.

However, engineering is not racing, and one cannot 'disqualify' a
machine for not conforming to old or existing rules. The only question
the engineer asks is whether the new type can do better than the old.
Can it accomplish what the old types cannot?

There is little profit in following the example of the Americans
who attempted to stage a regular 'butting match' between two locomotives—a large, steam-driven Mallet engine, and an electric
locomotive of far more modest dimensions. These were placed nose to
nose on the track, and set to push before a large crowd of spectators,
among whom, no doubt, odds were freely laid and taken.

It was found that when both locomotives started simultaneously,
the steam locomotive was at once pressed back. Its driver protested

Railwaymen took a long time to accustom themselves to the electric locomotive, that ugly
square, box of machinery on wheels. But this particular electric type, which hauls all the
numerous passenger trains over the Pennsylvania Railroad between New York, Philadelphia
and Washington, has such graceful, flowing lines, marked by golden stripes on a deep red
ground, that the most fastidious onlookers must approve.

A recent type of electric locomotive brought into service on the Southern Region of British Railways. It can haul goods trains of 1,000 tons, and passenger trains up to a speed of 75 m.p.h. Current is supplied through a conductor rail beside the track, and the engine, which weighs 105 tons, needs comparatively little servicing.

immediately, and not without reason. A steam locomotive has a direct drive to the coupled wheels, and, when starting, cannot develop full power until it is properly in motion. As soon as it is on full throttle, however, the steam driver insisted that it will easily get the better of its electric rival. This was agreed, and the steam locomotive was given a 'flying start'. The electric locomotive cut off power, acting merely as a stationary vehicle, and the steam locomotive pushed it along the track with gradually increasing speed. When it was running 'full out', its driver gave the signal and the electric locomotive went into action. To the great surprise of the 'steam fans' their giant slowed more and more, stopped, and was finally driven backwards at a fair speed in the easiest manner possible.

Such a contest, however interesting for the audience, is technically worthless. The electric locomotive draws all the power it needs from the overhead wires, and while a steam engine cannot be greatly overloaded, an electric motor can, at least for a very short time, be overloaded to twice its nominal power. Further, the weight of a steam engine is only partly carried by its driving wheels, while the electric machine can use all its weight for adhesion. The ordinary piston-driven steam locomotive also transmits its force to the driving wheels very unevenly—in particular, it can transmit no force at all at the two points where the cranks pass through the 'dead centres'. Electrical machinery has a particularly even turning movement, so that the driving wheels of an electric locomotive 'hold the road' better than those of the steam locomotive, which are liable to slip, especially when starting.

The generators in the power station send current into the overhead wires or conductor rails of the system, and the locomotives draw the necessary power from them to operate their driving motors. This process can, however, be reversed, thus providing a possibility of power-saving, which the steam-operated railways lack. Downhill, an ordinary train brakes by pressing brake-shoes against the wheels, developing much wasted heat in the process. An electric locomotive can be braked in quite another way. Instead of the motors turning the wheels, the wheels can turn the motors while running downhill. The motors then act as generators, feeding current back into the system. This is the principle of 'regenerative braking'.

The prospects, however, are less practical than theoretical. On the Ofoten Railway in Northern Norway, conditions are almost ideal for regenerative braking. The laden ore-trains run down from the frontier to the coast on an even gradient. As a rule, there is about one train an hour, all through the day. Full, heavy trains downhill, empty, light trains uphill. Practically an endless chain of trains in continuous operation. Surely the heavy trains should generate enough power to pull the empty trains upwards? Unfortunately, it was found that the electrical energy returned to the supply network by 'regenerative braking' was quite insufficient to drive the empty trains back. In experimental operation on the Ofoten line, only some 18–20 per cent of the power consumed by the heavy trains going down was available for the trains going up. This was insufficient to cover the high costs of installing full regenerative working of the line.

A modern 'tube' train on the London underground railway, Northern Line, coming into the open air at Golders Green. A normal train of seven carriages is driven by ten electric motors developing a total of 1,680 horse-power, and is capable of 60 m.p.h.

A powerful French electric locomotive designed to take alternating current at 25,000 volts direct from the French grid. It is used on the 170-mile line between Valenciennes and Thionville, which has been electrified at this voltage, with transformer stations every 35 to 50 miles. All earlier systems necessitated electricity sub-stations every 6 to 10 miles.

Where water-power is the principal source of electrical energy, and the waterfalls persist all the year round, the saving in kilowatt-hours is hardly worthwhile. Where steam-driven generators are used, every kilowatt-hour saved represents a corresponding saving in coal. In addition, the advantage lies not only in the recovery of current, but in the almost ideal braking action. On the Ofoten Railway, the application of all brake-shoes to all the wheels of the heavy wagons, throughout the long run downhill, causes enormous wear, both of brake-blocks and wheel tyres. With electrical braking, no metal parts are required to rub against one another; there is no friction. The wheels turn the motor armatures, and the armatures are braked by nothing more substantial or material than a magnetic field. The resistance of this field to the rotation of the armature is real and effective enough: it brakes the train.

It might be thought that a quick change-over to electric operation would be of the greatest advantage to countries such as Norway. In view of all the nation's resources of water-power it appears foolish to buy expensive coal, or still dearer oil, from abroad, instead of urgently proceeding with a general electrification of the railways. The problems arising are, however, exceptionally complex, and cannot be solved by any simple means. Electrification calls for expensive engineering structures and installations, the building of barrages and power-station buildings, transmission lines, transformers, and the like. When all this has been done, it is, however, possible to run a great number of trains daily at a cost little greater than that for one: the installation once completed, the water runs down the pipe-line, the power flows steadily

Ascending and descending cars pass at Fløy near Bergen. This cable railway, opened on 15th January, 1918, rises 300 yards in a length of 850 yards. At the upper end, the slope approaches 1 in 2. If necessary, the railway can carry nearly 400 passengers an hour. On such a railway, of course, everything humanly possible is done to exclude the possibility of the cable breaking. Just in case, and to reassure the timid, no less than three independent means of braking are provided: a hand-brake and a foot-brake, and an all-automatic brake—all of the jaw type, gripping the rails.

and uninterruptedly, day by day. The only remaining problem is to adjust daily consumption to the same, uniform rate.

If it is a question of running only a few trains daily it is probably cheaper to fire up a locomotive boiler at the appropriate times and places, instead of setting up a mighty generating and distributing plant, which gushes forth power in a regular flow, day and night. Only at a train-frequency of about six to seven each way, daily, do the economic arguments begin to tell in favour of electric traction. This, of course, is dependent on the unit prices forming the basis of the entire calculation, and is mentioned only to give an idea of the scope of the problem.

Take any railway time-table, and run down the pages. At the top is a long row of train times, spread over the whole day; but, following each column downwards, we find that many of them stop after only a short run. Train services are most frequent, therefore, only for short distances out of the great cities, and it is there that electrification is, in the first instance, justified by corresponding economic advantages. This, of course, is not an exhaustive solution of the problem.

Thus, while demands for early electrification of the Bergen Railway, for instance, over the high mountains of Norway become so insistent, it is not only economic considerations which have promoted the wish. True, the million pounds or so which would be saved by the transition from foreign coal to home-produced electricity are not to be despised, but that is not necessarily the most important consideration. Think what it represents to drive those coal-fired locomotives over the mountains, through 189 tunnels (with a total length of over 27 miles), appreciate what it means to the train crews to be free of their dependence on 'black diamonds' and run on the 'white coal' running down the mountain slopes! The passengers too, would not have to complain of the change.

The very first electric locomotive was built by a Scotsman named Davidson, about 1840, but the real pioneer was the German, Werner

This twin unit is the most powerful electric locomotive ever built, and is capable of developing no less than 11,400 horse-power. It works heavy passenger and freight trains up to the 3,786 ft. summit level of the Gothard line in Switzerland. Only one locomotive of this type has been built, however; later construction favours independent 12-wheel units of 6,000 horse-power each.

Siemens. In 1879, he built the first electric railway—even though only a miniature—which was the great sensation of the Industrial Exhibition of that year in Berlin. Although only a toy railway, it was in all respects the true ancestor of all modern electrical giants.

In one respect, the electric locomotive cannot compete with its steam-driven rival in appearance. All those features which make the steam locomotive so imposing to the eye of the layman are lacking in the electrical counterpart. It looks prosaically plain—a large railway carriage with panes of glass in front, behind which the driver is clearly seen and appears to have no more to do than a tram-driver. On the roof are two structures which make contact with the overhead wires from which the machine draws its power. In the 'third-rail' system, widely used for suburban traffic and now being extended to some main lines in Britain, a 'plough' or 'shoe' projecting from the undercarriage makes contact with a 'conductor rail'.

The inside is just as prosaic as the outside. The transformers and motors are completely cased-in, and even a glance inside the casings will not reveal much to the uninstructed. In front of the driver's seat there is an ordinary crank-handle, and on the wall above, some small handwheels; the other walls of the driver's compartment carry a few switches and fuse-boxes. The whole is scarcely imposing, nothing gives any impression of the thousands of horsepower which are controlled here. All in all, however, this very simplicity, the economy of the layout, plainly witnesses to the attainment of a technical masterpiece.

And now, see the giant start: easily and smoothly, whatever the load behind. In a very brief time, we are running at full speed. The electric locomotive has an acceleration rate greater than that of the steam locomotive. We come now to a long and steep uphill gradient. Involuntarily, we wait for the speed to drop, wait to hear our engine puffing and blowing, giving unmistakable signs of a hard task. Nothing of the sort happens—in fact we may possibly speed up a little. The driver has notched-up his handle, and the shrouded motors hum a little louder—that is all! But, it means a lot. It means that a tremendous quantity of energy, coming from a power-house many miles away, very likely, has passed through the current collector, and through the transformers, and has unleashed the full power of the driving motors. And so the gradient is forced with a power no other railway engine can develop.

Just behind the driver's cab are the electric motors. Their shafts

---

This shows the complete line of the cable railway, 4,491 yards long, which can carry 700 passengers per hour, 3,631 feet up from Davos in Switzerland, to the Parsenn, 8,737 feet above sea level. The gradient varies between 1 in 5 and 1 in 2. The Schwyz-Stoos railway, for comparison, also in Switzerland, has a ruling gradient of 1 in 1¼

One of the old City and South London underground railway trains. The early models developed about 50 horse-power and ran at 25 m.p.h. The carriages, known popularly as 'padded cells', had no windows.

carry toothed pinions, which transmit the power to large gear-wheels, from which it may pass through coupling rods to the driving wheels themselves. It is not unusual, as a matter of fact, to dispense with the coupling rods and make each motor drive its own axle. Behind the motor is the casing, with the large, oil circuit-breakers, which are used when the working current is switched on or off. There are, also, a number of auxiliary machines, such as the air compressors which operate the brakes, the warning siren, and the raising and lowering of the current-collecting 'bows', or 'pantographs'. Right at the far end of the locomotive are the transformers, which represent a major part of the total locomotive weight. On some railways, as in Norway, Sweden and Switzerland, the alternating current in the conductors, collected by the trains, is from 15,000 to 16,000 volts. This is stepped-down by the transformers, the actual voltage used ranging from 75 volts to 550 volts, the demand being supplied on the turning of a handle. The heating of electrically-drawn trains is generally, but not always, electrical.

In theory, an electric locomotive can be controlled quite automatically, but however it is done it must be controlled from some point or other. There is always a human hand and a human brain required, whether on the train or elsewhere. The object is, in any case, not the maximum of automatic control, but the maximum of safety. Experience shows that complete safety is not identical with the maximum of automatic control, but that the best results are obtained by a reasonable compromise between the two.

As a matter of fact, the automatic control equipment fitted in an electric locomotive is already sufficiently dangerous, or would be so a watchful human agent were not always in the background. When he current is 'on', and the train under way, the vehicle continues to un of its own accord. The electric energy passes through the collectors, s transformed, and goes to the motors with the correct voltage. The motors rotate, and the locomotive hums on its way. There is nothing to stop this continuing, and this is where the danger lies. Suppose the driver, sitting alone in his cab, begins to do something else, to think of other things—of home, of his health, or of the pleasanter sides of life; or suppose he simply dozes off, or even falls ill or faints before he can summon aid! He omits to do something of vital importance. And the train rolls on.

There is a way of countering this danger. The safeguard is this, that even an *omission* by the driver—even what he does *not* do—can be made to stop the train. He has on his controller handle, or wheel, a button, which he must keep pressed down all the time the train is running. Thus, if he should forget his job or faint, or merely let go of the handle, he would automatically release the button and stop the train. In Britain, the button is replaced by a short lever known as the 'dead man's handle', which must be kept depressed.

This safeguard operates by merely stopping the train safely. There is no violent pull-up; should the driver just nod at his post it is not necessary for the whole train to come to an abrupt standstill. When the pressure on the button slackens, the train still runs on for some 100 to 200 yards before the brakes go on automatically, and, before this happens, a bell begins to ring, so that, if it is only a case of momentary inattention, the driver can wake up before anything drastic happens. A similar device on diesel-electric locomotives is worked by the foot and is called the 'dead man's treadle'.

In electric railway operation, another automatic safety device can be used for the purpose of preventing trains over-running—at least for any appreciable distance—signals set at danger. As soon as a danger signal has been passed the locomotive receives some form of electric pulse, which first acts as a warning and then, if necessary, stops the train automatically.

Different types of locomotive can be compared or classified in

A geared steam-turbine express passenger locomotive—or 'turbomotive'—built by the London, Midland and Scottish Railway in 1935. It ran some of the fastest trains, but there were many failures, and it has since been scrapped.

One of the first European gas-turbine-electric locomotives is No. 18000 of British Railways, built by the Swiss firm of Brown-Boveri for service over the Western Region. It weighs 115 tons and is rated at 2,500 h.p

various ways. There is, first, the division into steam-operated and motor-driven (diesel-electric or all-electric) locomotives. This is a nominal, rather than a technical classification. Even nominally the distinction is somewhat tenuous, since steam-engines, diesel engines, and electric motors are all essentially 'prime movers'.

There is, however, a profound difference between two groups of prime movers: electric on the one hand, and steam or internal-combustion on the other hand. The two last-named are reciprocating engines; *i.e.*, the piston, moving to and fro, is the power element. The electric motor is a rotary engine; its power element is a 'rotor', which is continuously influenced by an electro-magnetic field, receiving a continuous 'turning moment', causing it to rotate. This is a particularly suitable drive for a locomotive, which requires to move as smoothly as possible. A locomotive driven by a reciprocating engine requires special transmission gear—piston-rod and crank—to convert reciprocating into rotary motion.

The electric motor is, however, not the only rotating prime mover. There is another type which, furthermore, is driven by the combustion of a fuel (as are steam and diesel engines)—the steam or gas turbine. The steam turbine, first built by Sir Charles Parsons and patented in

A larger and heavier gas-turbine-electric unit built by the British firm of Metropolitan-Vickers for comparison with the Swiss machine is No. 18100 of British Railways, which also has been at work on the Western Region. The weight is 130 tons and the h.p. 3,000.

The famous 'Fifty', or X-50, as it is officially listed, on the Union Pacific Railroad, a gas-turbo-electric locomotive, the tests of which under ordinary traffic conditions have attracted great attention in railway circles. The trials were exhaustive. The locomotive was worked through the Cajon Pass, the worst gradient on the Union Pacific, from Los Angeles up to Salt Lake City, with a mile of goods trucks behind it. The amazing fact is that the machinery —including gas-turbine, electric generator, and motors—weighs only 6 pounds per horse-power developed, or about half the weight for a diesel locomotive. It consumes more fuel than the latter, however, although of a lower and much cheaper grade—the heaviest refinery residues. Nor is it particularly silent-running; it whistles and roars, like a jet-plane. The 4,500 horse-power in its engine room makes more noise than passengers would approve. But the Union Pacific is building a number more of these gas-turbine-electric units, of still greater power, and the noise problem will also doubtless be mastered in due course.

1884, is already a 'conventional' engine type. It is widely used in ships, and has also been tried for locomotives but not always with fruitful results. Even Sir William Stanier's geared turbine Pacific-type loco-motive, built at Crewe for the L.M.S. in 1935, though it did a good deal of useful work, was not multiplied and was eventually scrapped.

The newest type is the gas turbine, already known from its use in jet aircraft. The gas turbine has been used at sea, and is now gaining a footing in locomotive construction; it is, in the opinion of many, the prime mover of the future. It is an exceedingly simple engine consisting principally of three main parts: an air compressor, a combustion chamber, and a turbine. The compressed air is provided for the com-bustion of the fuel (liquid, or even powdered) in the combustion chamber, whence the combustion gases issue at very high pressure and temperature, and strike the turbine blades. In the gas turbine loco-motive the turbine then drives a generator which supplies electricity to traction motors, exactly as in the diesel-electric engine.

Compared with the diesel engine, the gas turbine has many advant-

Already in 1811, Blenkinsop had built this locomotive with a toothed driving wheel engaging a cogged rail; he maintained that no locomotive could run on smooth rails! He was wrong, but can be credited with the rack-and-pinion principle of mountain railway working.

ages for use in railway locomotives. In coal-producing countries there is the welcome possibility of running gas turbines on pulverized coal. Nor is the gas turbine fastidious in regard to oil fuel; it cheerfully swallows the crudest 'crude', the thickest and cheapest petroleum available. It runs at a high speed, which is not in itself advantageous, but, by comparison with the diesel engine, its speed can be varied over a wide range (from some 6–7,000 r.p.m., down to 2–3,000 r.p.m.) without great difficulty, and this simplifies the construction of transmission gears.

On the other hand, a great drawback of the gas turbine is the exceedingly high temperature of the combustion gases which is necessary if the turbine is to develop its fullest possible efficiency. This temperature can be reduced somewhat before the gases impinge on the turbine blades, but not quite sufficiently to avoid harmful action on the blade metal. The gases are therefore partly cooled by air from the compressor, but this heating up and cooling down wastes energy, and efficiency is decreased. Much ingenuity has been used in finding metal alloys capable of withstanding the unavoidable high temperatures.

The first gas turbine locomotive was built in 1939 by Brown-Boveri Ltd. jointly with the L.S.M. of Winterthur, with financial assistance from the Swiss Federal Railways. It went into service in 1943, and was later used in France, while America was running its own Alco-G. E. gas turbine locomotive on the Union Pacific Railroad in 1948. In Britain, Metropolitan-Vickers have developed a gas turbine locomotive which is likely to compete with the Brown-Boveri system, and Sweden already has gas turbine locomotives in regular service.

In 'the order of appearance', as theatre playbills have it, locomotive types are: steam, electric, diesel and gas-turbine. This classification by historical stages is an alternative to the one already given, and yet another instructive classification sometimes used is based on a quite different principle. There are adhesion locomotives, running directly with smooth wheels on smooth rails, without any ingenious devices, and rack locomotives, which move themselves forward by a more complicated arrangement—cog-wheels and toothed racks, or the like.

If we firmly lock the brakes of an ordinary locomotive, and raise one end of the track more and more steeply, it will keep its position until the gradient reaches about 1 in 4. That is quite a steep gradient. Even the famous 'corkscrew' ski-ing track at Holmenkollen in its worst

View inside the mechanism of a Fell locomotive; showing the two horizontal driving wheels which are pressed from either side firmly against the double-headed, special central rail. In this manner, additional adhesion is obtained, enabling the locomotive to ascend gradients up to 1:10. On horizontal sections of the line, or easy gradients, the central rail is omitted, and the engine runs in the ordinary manner.

part is no steeper. However, the locomotive cannot run *up* such a steep slope, whatever its horse-power. As soon as it starts to move contact between the wheels and the rails becomes worse and worse owing to the motion and vibration; friction decreases, and the locomotive simply slips backwards. Hence, a gradient of 1 in 4 is too much for an ordinary train. The steepest gradient worked by ordinary adhesion methods is about 1 in 14.

Thus, the simple adhesion locomotive is no great hill climber. On the other hand, there is often good and sufficient need for the railway to climb hills, and it may be necessary or advantageous to cut out all the loops and windings necessary for an ordinary railway. A number of different types of locomotive suitable for climbing hills have therefore been designed. As might be expected, these are not high-speed engines, and hardly seem to belong in a book dealing with the age of speed. They will, therefore, merely be mentioned to complete our survey.

The tractive force of a locomotive depends, as we have already seen, on the load on the driving wheels and the coefficient of friction between steel and steel. If the adhesion weight is 100 tons, and the coefficient 0·25, the tractive force is 25 tons; if the frictional coefficient is only 0·20, the tractive force is 20 tons, etc. Locomotives for mountain railways must be small and light. The tractive force is correspondingly low. It could be asked, however, if it is really necessary to use the weight of the locomotive to press the wheels against the train?

Fell, an Englishman, found this was not so. He laid a third, double-headed rail between the two running rails, and pressed two *horizontal* driving wheels against it on either side, as shown on page 143. This pressure is quite independent of the adhesion weight of the locomotive and can be increased to any extent required to enable the locomotive to pull itself up a steep gradient. The Fell system still uses the adhesion principle, since it uses friction and not toothed wheels. This is the only one of the mountain-climbing locomotives which can also run on an ordinary track, like any other locomotive; the central rail is laid only where the gradient becomes too steep. While the Mont Cenis railway was being driven *through* the Alps, Fell offered to build a railway *over* the Fréjus Pass. The tunnel cost nearly six million pounds. Fell's railway cost (at that time) no more than half a million. Engineers have stated that if the Fell system had already existed before the Mont Cenis tunnel had been started, the tunnel would never have been

---

This cable railway, from Lugano on the lake of the same name up to Monte Brè, looks more terrifying than it really is. Ropes and cables may break; but the instant they do so, their tension stops, and this releases automatic grips which lock the car firmly to the rails. While the line is steep it is safe compared with the risks we take in lifts every day of our lives.

built, but they were, of course, wrong, as the heavy modern traffic over this main line could never have been handled over such steep gradients. Though Fell's railway was actually built, and carried 150,000 passengers over the Alps in addition to goods and mails between 1868 and 1871, when the tunnel was finished the contract was terminated.

This system can be used only for gradients up to about 1 in 10. When the Rigi Railway in Switzerland was planned in 1869, however, gradients of up to 1 in 5 had to be contemplated. The system adopted there harks back to Blenkinsop's old idea. In 1811, he built a colliery line near Leeds, using a rack rail and toothed driving wheel, fully believing this to be essential even on a horizontal track. He was wrong, but later, on the Rigi, his idea bore fruit. In principle, the locomotives of the Rigi Railway follow Blenkinsop's design, with the difference that the rack rail is laid between the running rails.

Gradients continued to increase. When the Swiss attacked Mont Pilatus with a railway, they had to raise the line 5,300 feet in a distance of $2\frac{5}{8}$ miles. This implies an *average* gradient of 1 in 3; but, on the last and steepest section, it had to be 1 in 2. Even that was possible with a rack railway, although not on the same system as that used on the Rigi. In this case the rack rails were laid sideways instead of upright, and engaged by horizontal toothed wheels, which grip the rack securely on both sides.

Here, however, we are already approaching operating conditions in which it is hardly possible to speak of a railway proper, or of railway locomotives in the ordinary sense. It is, of course, always possible to climb anywhere if there is sufficient need. In an ordinary lift, the 'gradient' is 1 in 0, and there is nothing steeper in the world. But these are not *railways* to the railway engineer. They are merely loads being hoisted—dead loads on the end of a rope. They may be called *cable* ways, since they use carriages on wheels and run on rails; but a railway proper consists essentially of self-propelled vehicles, or trains of vehicles, running on their own 'road'—the permanent way. The fact that the Fløy 'railway' in Bergen has a gradient of 1 in 2, and the Virgl line in the Tyrol a maximum of 1 in 1·73, does not impress your true railway-man, who takes offence if even funicular or telpher transporters are called 'railways'. They have neither wheels nor rails—they are mere boxes hanging on a rope and pulled by a string.

CHAPTER V

SAFETY FIRST

"Safety first" is the cry of our generation. In this era of science and engineering, a cry of fear arises from thousands and thousands, alarmed lest the monsters of the age of speed turn and crush them. "They must be stopped, something must be done before it is too late." The plea is—Safety first and foremost, even at the cost of speed and progress!

This craving for safety and physical security developed as soon as mechanically-propelled vehicles appeared in their thousands on roads and highways which had hitherto been relatively safe for the peaceful citizen. The drawbacks and dangers, the inconvenience and irritation, the frequent and terrible accidents, all created a growing suspicion that scientific and engineering development had become a danger, a source of misfortune and insecurity.

There is a grain of truth in this; the majority of the accidents we read about in the papers are 'technical' faults—running-down, collision, breakdown, explosion. The account is, however, not so one-sided. Science and engineering, the whole vast complex of physical and material attainments, is a shield and an aid to mankind, a protection from the dangers threatening from without. Humanity is immeasurably better equipped to protect its health and livelihood from all the adverse influences of Nature, to conduct its communal life in peace and amity, in the present 'engineering age' than in any other epoch of history.

In this defensive war against external, common dangers, from bacteria to earthquakes, flood, famine and pestilence, transport and speed are powerful weapons. We can attack and counter-attack, where necessary, more rapidly and effectively than ever before. The increase in speed of communication, of transport and travel, is the foundation of a more rational organization of human life, and has reduced our formerly scattered humanity to a more compact community in which no unit need consider itself forlorn, but can rely on speedy and sure help from other units.

It must be confessed, however, that while the technical development of speed in transport and communication has given effective help and protection against *external* foes and dangers, it has itself given birth to many and varying *internal* perils. The weapon itself becomes a danger to the user. It is necessary, therefore, that science and engineering, while themselves increasing their scope and efficiency, develop their own safeguards, their own 'security services' against the latent dangers which threaten those dependent on them. Justifiably, the demand is made that progress and safety shall go hand in hand. It is unnecessary and undesirable to allow progress and development to reach a stage at which 'Safety!' becomes a panic cry; on the contrary, while development continues safety considerations should be constantly borne in mind. As a shining example to be followed, the manner in which the railways have solved this dual problem of combining efficiency with safety deserves honourable mention.

It can be claimed that in no other sphere has the work of developing effective safeguards been conducted so systematically and purposefully as in railway engineering and operation. What are the accidents and disasters against which these safeguards are to give protection? First and foremost, the danger to the passenger from the railway itself, and then such external dangers as we have already illustrated. These included the defences required by railways to protect themselves from the dangers of the high slopes in mountain country, from frost and ice in Alaska, from the jungle in Africa. However, only a fraction of the railway safety services is deployed on this external front.

The word 'collision', which appears so often in the news reports of disasters, has acquired a new connotation. Of course, there have always been collisions, but they have not been great disasters. If two stage-coaches crashed together at a bend in the road, the results were seldom serious—and the occurrence was not too frequent. 'Collision', as a catastrophe, has appeared only in the age of speed. The higher the speed, the greater the danger of collision, and—which is the essential point—the more disastrous the consequences. It is worth while dwelling a little on this relationship between speed and consequences. Theoretically, if the speed of a train or car is doubled, the capacity for doing damage in the event of a collision is quadrupled. The risk increases

---

At a derailment in Iowa, U.S.A., forty-five goods wagons were pitched down the slope. The relatively small damage they have suffered is a consequence of the substantial construction of modern railway vehicles; but is also due to the fact that the five loads of 16-in. cannon shells included failed to explode!

as the square of the speed—twice the speed, four times the danger—
thrice the speed, nine times the danger—and so on. The reader ma
profitably take this sequence a few steps further. The reason for th
ominous development is relatively simple. The destructive effect of
collision depends essentially on the energy lost or absorbed at th
instant of contact.

Whence comes this energy? Let us assume that a railway train wit
a total weight of 1,000 tons is running at 50 miles an hour. This gia
in motion acquires a 'kinetic energy', or *vis viva* as it is sometimes calle
of the order of 723,300 million foot-pounds, purely by reason of i
speed. If two such trains collide, their united energy is nearly 3 milli
million foot-pounds, or 1,500 million foot-tons. A few seconds lat
those engines and trucks are lying demolished on the line, and a
this energy has been absorbed. It has been used to bend, break, twi
crush and destroy everything animate and inanimate within reac
Suppose the whole disastrous destruction is completed in 5 seconds. A
will be remembered, one horse-power is equivalent to 550 ft./lb. p
second, or 2,750 foot-pounds in 5 seconds. Thus, the equivalent of th
kinetic energy of the colliding trains is represented by some 1,0
million horse-power. The result would be the same as if we let stea
hammers of 1,000 million horse-power pound the trains for five secon

Now, the kinetic energy of a moving body (these trains) increas
with the square of the speed. Above, we assumed a speed of 50 m.p.
for each train. With two trains colliding head-on at separate spee
of 100 m.p.h., therefore, the energy would be not twice but four tim
as great, and equivalent to 4,000 million horse-power! These are f
from trifling forces which the railways have brought into the worl
to the peril of innocent millions. It is not surprising, therefore, that t
most rigorous precautions are demanded to mitigate, as far as possib
the risk of such disastrous accidents.

On our first considering the problem of avoiding collision, it do
not seem so difficult to prevent two trains from running into each oth
between stations. Apparently, it is only necessary for the engine driv
to keep a good lookout, and stop as soon as they see a train in fro
This was, in fact, all that was done in the early days of railways: tra
were started on their way at suitable time intervals, and the drivers to
care of the rest. At first, a man carrying a red flag rode ahead of t
train, to warn people off the line—a practice long since abandon
The engine-driver no longer has a man ahead to clear the way; but
is still impossible to leave everything to him. With present train spee
an express train requires some 800 yards (half a mile) to come to r
from full speed; in fact, at a mile a minute and more, this 'braki

he machine age has already developed its own 'musical form'—a keen appreciation of the hole gamut of sounds emitted by running machinery. Here, an expert 'listens in' to a k locomotive. Like a good, old-fashioned general practitioner, he uses a form of stethoscope, even though he does not ask the locomotive to 'say ninety-nine'.

ngth' is no less than 1,000–1,200 yards. This will give us food for ought next time the express is pounding along and the mile posts ash by. What force is necessary to stop the speeding train without a

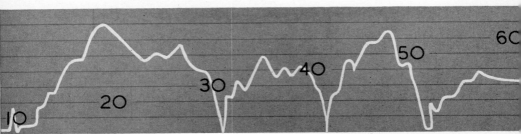

The speedometer of a motor car shows the speed at any instant, nothing more. Some drive are only too glad that it indicates a flat 30 m.p.h.—when 'the other fellow' crashes into the Others may be glad that it fails to record that '50' in a built-up area. The driver of t Swiss locomotive has no option, his speedometer has an infallible memory. On the strip paper which the regulations oblige him to put into the instrument, the speedometer recor a graph of the speed at every instant of the run. The strip shows that he reached 70 on

Steel v. Wood. In a collision near Quebec, Canada, a steel-built passenger coach bored its way through a wooden carriage (although this was sheathed with steel) and split it in two. Such accidents, which in this case cost nine dead and fifty-five injured, would be much less dangerous, if all trains were of steel.

thousand yards? If something which cannot get out of the way instantly appears on the line within this distance, a collision is certain. The prospect is even worse if the 'obstacle' is a moving train coming from the opposite direction. In such a case, *both* engine-drivers must have seen each other not less than a mile away, if collision is to be avoided.

In such conditions, it is abundantly clear that safety precautions cannot be left to the engine driver alone. It is not sufficient, even, to send out trains on the line at intervals of, *e.g.*, 10 minutes. The train in front may have had trouble and stopped on the line; if the following driver does not notice this in time, an accident is inevitable.

A time-interval alone cannot, therefore, prevent collision. The only remaining remedy is to introduce a space-interval, a distance or length between trains; means must be used to prevent them from ever treading on each other's heels. This principle, which is now used on practically every railway in the world, was first devised for use in tunnels. At a relatively early date a train was prevented from entering a tunnel until the preceding train had emerged. When a train entered, a signal at the tunnel-mouth was set to 'Stop', and was not changed to 'Go' or 'Clear' until the message had come from the far end of the tunnel that the train had passed. There was then never more than one train in the tunnel at a time.

This is the 'absolute block system' in all its simplicity. The line is divided into 'block sections', and measures are taken to prevent more

An ambulance coach on the Norwegian State Railways. The sick bay has three tiers of stretchers; beyond is the operating room. This vehicle is for use in major accidents, and forms part of a 'breakdown train' always standing ready at some central point on the railway.

than one train being in any section at the same time. A train 'entering section' has the road closed behind it by signals, which are not released until the train is 'out of section' at the other end. The railway signalman evidently believes in the old prescription: "Always shut the door behind you."

The following diagram shows a railway line working in one direction only, from station A to station B. The line is divided into four block sections, by three section boxes with corresponding signalling equipment. A train wishing to leave station A is not released until that station receives the message from block signal Box 1, that the preceding train is 'out of section' and the line is clear up to there. The train

A line equipped for one-way traffic with four block sections. The train is proceeding from Station A to Station B, and has entered the second block section. The nearest signal *behind* the train is at danger, and cannot be set to 'clear' (arm slanting upwards), until the train has left the second block section and entered the third.

starts, and presently reaches signal Box 1, which it is not allowed to pass until that signal is set at 'line clear'—which will be when Box 1 receives the message from Box 2 that the preceding train has passed there. When our train (the second) passes Box 1, the signalman there sets his signal at 'danger', and thus 'shuts the door' behind the train. This is the position shown in the drawing: the train is in the second section, and the signal behind it, set at danger (arm horizontal). Box 2 has had the message from Box 3 that the section between Box 2 and Box 3 is unoccupied, and has, therefore, set its own signal to 'clear' (arm slanting upwards).

What happens if these messages, exchanged between the signalmen in the different boxes, are missed, or misunderstood? This is obviously

An ambulance carriage of the Norwegian State Railways. The sick bay has three tiers of stretchers; beyond is the operating room. This vehicle is for use in war, or at major accidents, and forms part of a 'breakdown train' always standing ready at some central point on the railway.

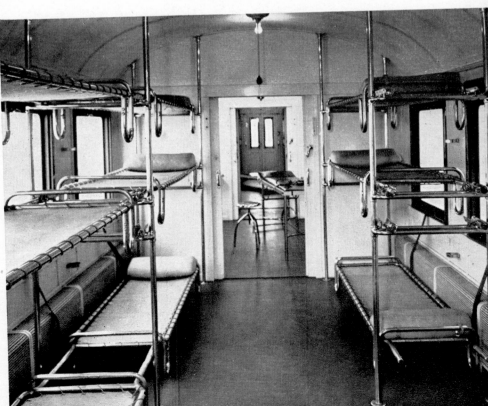

A railway accident which is probably unique. It happened on 22nd December, 1889, at Strömmen in Norway; the boiler of locomotive No. 11 exploded, with the fantastic result that the locomotive made a 'standing jump' which is surely a world record, and fell, upside down, on top of locomotive No. 36. When the station staff recovered from their shock, and reconnoitred the position, they found No. 11 had well and truly landed on No. 36, which was so little damaged that it could steam off to the shops with its strange rider.

a danger factor which must be eliminated. Hence, such messages are passed, not in words, but as electric pulses. These pulses speak in very plain language—they release or lock the handles controlling the signals on the line. The signalman simply cannot make a false move. Before the train can leave the station, A, the 'home starting signal' S, must be at 'clear'. When the train, on its way out, passes a certain point on the track, it releases an automatic device which returns the starting signal to 'danger'. It is automatically locked in that position, and, *for a certain period, cannot be moved to the 'clear' position.* Before this is possible the following events must have occurred.

First, the appropriate railway official at Station A must work the 'block instrument'. He presses a button and turns the handle of a small electric inductor. The resulting pulse passes along the line wires and warns Box 1 that the train is 'approaching section'. When the train 'enters section' at Box 1, the signalman there does the same: he presses a button and operates an inductor. This sends an electric pulse ahead of the train, to Box 2, giving warning of the approach of the train. Secondly, a pulse goes back to Station A, and there releases the locked 'home starter'; which can now, and only now, be 'cleared' to allow the

A Modern 'Buckeye' automatic coupling which dispenses with the rather dangerous necessity of stepping between two railway vehicles to 'hook on'.

next train to leave that station. Now also, the first block section is free, and all chance of a collision has been avoided. The process is repeated as the train travels along. No signal box can change its block signal from 'danger' to 'clear', until the message has been received that the line ahead is in fact clear. No change is possible, since it is that message itself which releases the lever controlling the signal.

This sounds highly satisfactory, but suppose the signalman in Box 1 should forget to put his signal to danger when the train has passed; could not another train then enter the section between block points 1 and 2, and cause an accident? Even that cannot happen, for such a following train cannot leave station A. It will be remembered

This is the man who controls the 'driverless' trains on the Post Office Underground Railway in London.

that Box I has to report back to the station before a train can be released from there, and the signalman in Box I cannot report back *until* his signal is at 'danger'. His instrument is locked, and can only be released by putting the signal to 'danger'. Thus, there is complete and *automatic* control, and every train is covered in the rear by a signal at danger. Station A cannot release a train without action by Box I, and Box I cannot act until and unless the signal there is at danger.

There are, however, still possibilities of mistakes, which the intelligent reader may already have discerned. Assume that the signalman in Box I takes a nap, wakes suddenly and, with a guilty conscience, suspects uneasily that he has heard a train passing. He jumps up, puts his signal at danger, and rings back to station A to 'clear the block'. That station, of course, will now be able to release its home starting signal and send the next train on its way. The drowsy signalman has been mistaken, however; the first train has not passed, but has been held up on the way by a mechanical fault. An accident seems inevitable. Railway signal engineers, however, have already foreseen this possibility and guarded against it. Should the sleepy signalman try

This miniature railway is the only one of its kind in the world. It runs at a depth of sixty-five feet under London streets between Paddington and Whitechapel. It carries no passengers— only mailbags. This electrical, centrally controlled railway without drivers or train guards, carries 11½ million postal packets every year. The bags from the post offices are sent down chutes and are sorted into containers on the platform on the left. These can easily be wheeled into the carriages of the trains, which are despatched at four-minute intervals.

to send off his misleading message that the train has passed, he will find his block instrument locked against him. It is only released automatically, by the passage of the train itself.

An exceedingly simple method of controlling trains on single-line railways was developed in Britain. It originated with the organization of special 'train pilots', who accompanied each train from crossing place to crossing place. Each pilot had charge of one section between crossing places (usually stations). No train was allowed in that section without a pilot.

In such manner, it was ensured that in no case could there be more than one train on the line between these two stations. As traffic increased however, the pilot became too busy, spending whole days travelling to and fro on locomotives—for the core of the idea was that there should be only *one* pilot in each section. This was a dreary and profitless occupation, since the pilot *did* nothing! He only travelled on the trains, a dummy, shuttling to and fro. It was true humanity, therefore, to release him before he was ripe for a mental hospital, and to replace him by an inanimate 'train staff'. This staff is handed to the engine-driver at the one station and returned by him to the station master at the other end of the section, and so forth. While the train staff was in his possession, the engine-driver knew that there *could* be no other train in the section, since there is only one train staff in existence for each section. This plan requires, however, that there shall be an equal number of trains running on the line in each direction, alternately, since otherwise the staff would remain held up at one of the end stations of each section. The single staff was, therefore, replaced by several, locked in frames which are in electrical communication from station to station. Only one staff at a time can be used. When one is 'out', all the others remain locked until the first staff is replaced in the frame at the other station.

In the latest form of single-line train working the problem is solved by signals. The arrangement is somewhat more complicated than for a double-line railway, but follows the same essential principle of the 'closed door'. Readers who have had their fill of 'blocks' may now skip ahead to p. 165. The more seriously minded may like to solve the 'crossing-junction problems' which follow.

In the first case, for two-way traffic there must be two sets of signals two at each block point, one for each direction, as shown in the sketch. Since trains cannot pass *over* each other, a crossing loop must be arranged at each crossing point of a single-line railway. The situation shown in the sketch is that one train is standing in the passing siding, travelling from B to A, while a train is approaching the crossing from the other

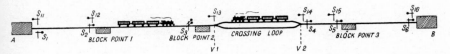

Single-line railway with traffic in both directions. The crossing loop, V_1 to V_2, is to enable trains to pass each other. There are, further, two sets of signals: S_1 to S_6 for the direction from A to B; S_{11} to S_{16} for the direction from B to A. One train is standing in the crossing loop but cannot proceed, since the signal S_{13} is at danger. Signal S_3, on the other hand, is clear and indicates to the train coming from Station A that it can safely run through the crossing. Only after it has cleared the crossing can the waiting train be given 'clear' on Signal S_{13}.

direction, A to B. The signal S_2, behind the latter train, is at danger, which is correct, while signal S_3 is open. The train can thus enter the unoccupied track at the crossing. At the same time, signal S_{13} is at danger, and prevents the train running *towards* A from proceeding. This is a most important requirement. While S_3 is 'clear', S_{13} cannot be touched and remains at danger. Only after the train coming *from* A has entered the crossing loop and been covered in the rear by signal S_3 'on', can the signal S_{13} be pulled off, to allow the other train to proceed. These two signals, S_3 and S_{13} are, therefore, so interlocked that they cannot both be 'off' simultaneously. They are 'hostile' signals, and such pairs are frequently used.

The signalling problems we have dealt with above have, of course, little in common with the difficult and complicated problems involved in safeguarding traffic within the areas of large terminal and junction stations. Oslo East, a relatively small terminus, has 74 points. The largest railway station on the Continent of Europe, Roma Termini, has 736 levers requiring attention. Some 500 trains daily thread the maze of lines, with all the switching movements which this entails. If an engine-driver were to attempt to find his own way to the correct platform, he would take hours to work his way through the confusion.

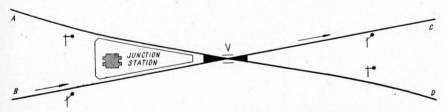

A crossing of two lines 'on the level', considered by railwaymen to require the most careful protection. Observing the set of the signals, which are always on the right hand of the driver, it is seen that there is a 'clear line' for a train from B to C, while the line is blocked for incoming trains proceeding both from A and from D.

The lines of rails converge on the station, under the signal gantry. As the points are set in the foreground, the train will turn off to the right, as shown by the white arrow on the counter-weight of the points arm. These signals are of a Continental type.

However, everything here is controlled centrally, from a single signal box. This is the heart and brain of a large station. Here, all the nerve filaments come together, and from here, run along the wires all the electric pulses which set the correct points, clear the way and operate the guiding and protecting signals for all the hundreds of trains arriving and departing. It is fantastic to think that this all really takes place, in every large station, in a regular and orderly manner, hour after hour, day by day, throughout the year; that all this safety mechanism interlocks so perfectly, that all trains going to and fro have their paths correctly planned and cleared and are completely safeguarded from collision with each other.

In such a signal box, the first thing seen is a long row of handles or levers. Moving one such handle from one position to another causes points to be set in a certain fashion out in the 'yard', and signals to be pulled on or off. From the signal box, everything is made ready; its levers clear the correct path, set the road for all incoming and outgoing trains, control all the warning signals. The men who work in the box turn handles in rapid sequence, move levers to and fro, the whole day long. Each of these movements can affect the life or death of hundreds, and for this very reason a host of safeguards, locks and interlocks has been devised and operates its own small miracles.

A train is standing at a platform, ready to leave in a few minutes. The station starting signal is, however, still on, and no guard's whistle, no waving of coloured flags or lamps can make the driver pass that warning 'starter', as it is called. It is controlled from the signal box; but the signalman cannot simply move the lever that will pull off the starting signal. First he must 'set the road' for the outgoing train—*i.e.*, all the points it must pass over on its way through and out of the station, on to its proper running line, must be set in the appropriate positions. First, therefore, all the levers moving all these points must be set correctly before the starting signal lever can be moved to 'off'. This already sounds very complicated, but railway passengers should be grateful for the precautions. In some Continental countries the 'starter' cannot be moved, however, until another 'master' lever has been moved. This *locks* all the pre-set point-levers (and, maybe, signal levers) in their positions, and prevents them from being interfered with until the particular train has actually passed and is clear of the station. Even that is not enough. The points, which are released when the starting signal is pulled off, may have been wrongly set before they were locked. The starting arm is, therefore, also interlocked, and it cannot be pulled off by the man in the signal box until a third, and last, safety-lock is released—the 'platform starter'. It is not possible to see all the platforms from the signal box, nor to know whether all is in order there. That is a matter for the station master or platform inspector. When all is clear for starting on the platform, the platform starter is pulled off and the signal box can release the remaining signal and let the train go. The guard's whistle, and a wave of his flag, permit the driver to start it from the platform.

As the train passes a particular point on the line, an electric circuit is closed, and the home signal is pulled on automatically. This protects the train from the rear. In the signal box, the corresponding lever is still 'off', but is put back by the signalman. Meanwhile, the train continues on its way, along the 'road' which has been made for it. If the home signal for this road were not electrically blocked, the men in the box might accidentally pull it off and thus release the points before the train had passed clear of the station, which could cause a serious accident. The electric block prevents this, and can be released automatically by the train passing over an electric contact outside the danger zone, *i.e.*, the station area, and energizing an electric circuit controlling the train indicator arm in the box. The levers for all the points concerned can now be freed, and the points reset to form other in and out roads for further trains.

As we have seen, the outgoing train itself automatically sets the home starting signal at danger as soon as the train has left the platform. The corresponding lever in the signal box also moves to 'on'. This can happen at any time: the lever is not locked when open, and thus the necessary opportunity remains with the signalmen of setting the starting signal back to danger at any time, should they discover some obstacle to the free passage of the train. Once this lever is moved to 'danger' however, after the train has departed, it remains locked by a mechanical device, since, in theory, the signalmen would not be in a position to release it until the train had passed into the next block section;

A pair of rail points, or a 'switch' as it is sometimes called. In the position shown, the road is clear for running straight through. If the points are moved so that the left-hand tongue moves against the left-hand rail and the right-hand tongue moves away from the right-hand rail, the train will turn on to the track bending away to the right. Such points are worked from signal boxes, and enable a 'road' to be correctly set for any passing train.

then the lever is pulled off by the setting of the home signal at block 1 to danger. For reasons of safety, this would appear essential. In actual fact, however, this first lock *is* released, by the action of the station signal box in 'offering' the train to the next block section. When that section 'accepts' the train, the starter lock is re-established (this time electrically) and is released only when block section 1 signals 'train in section' and simultaneously sets its own home signal to 'danger'. Now the station is cleared and the signal box can bring forward the next train.

It should be explained that the foregoing goes further than much British practice in the ordinary lineside signal boxes. In the practice of some Continental countries, the safeguards and safety measures *are* intricate, consisting of a great number of small, closely related steps; but the broad lines are now easily discerned. In order to ensure the safe passage of a train over a certain stretch of line, a number of different operations have to be performed, strictly in the correct order. The effect of a preceding operation must persist until the next step is taken. Everything is, therefore, interlocked from step to step: every operator must report back what has been done, and meanwhile he is debarred from further action. He locks the door and passes the key to the next man to unlock.

In addition to these operating safeguards, however, there are several other points to be watched if absolute safety is to be assured. The centralization of all threads of the action in one signal box has one weak spot. The points and signals are thus being operated by remote control. If the signalman in the box proceeds to set points 653, he does not approach the points directly: he moves a lever. From this lever, a long wire or an electric cable runs to points 653, somewhere out on the line. If all works well, the points are set or changed correctly in accordance with the position of the lever in the signal box. But what if all does not go well? Then, only the correct *lever* has been moved—small comfort for those injured in the ensuing smash. The signalman is unable actually to see the points he is putting over. Means are used, therefore, to ensure that the mechanism operated out on the line *reports back* that the action of the lever in the signal box has produced the right effect—that the order has been obeyed.

In an electrically interlocking system, this is simply arranged, as follows. When the points move into the correct position, they work a contact. When the whole road has been set, all the contacts involved should be closed, and the whole should form an electric circuit. If there is the smallest fault, anywhere, the circuit is incomplete and the final lever by which the whole pre-set road is locked cannot be moved; thus warning the signalman to take steps to put matters right.

The main signal box at Roma Termini, the central railway station of the Italian capital. The levers on the instrument panel control 736 points in the station area, with their corresponding signals. From this 'brain' of the system, the 'nerves' formed by the electric wires transmit messages which set the road correctly for each train and safeguard its passage by directing and protecting signals.

It is obviously a great advantage to the modern railway signalman to have an electrically-equipped signal box, and dispense with the old, heavy hand-levers, working on many yards of wire cable. A glance at the illustration of the main signal box at Roma Termini, however, will make it plain that this change was essential. Even though the signalmen can now comfortably handle their points and signal levers without undue physical exertion, there is enough else to do. A glance at the 'track diagram' on the wall above the levers will show that the signalmen must give their full attention to finding a 'road' through this labyrinth.

In a modern station, like Rome, the system of operation is much simpler than that described with so much detail above. For instance, the old inductor handles which had to be turned briskly to work the block instruments have been replaced by thumb-switches and push-buttons. One feature remains, however; each separate pair of points throughout the path of the train is still controlled individually by a separate action of the signalman in the box.

The whole complex system has evolved, step by step, over many years, and not a loop-hole remains to be closed. The system is fool-proof and complete. But this does not mean that it is the only possible

The man on whom all depends ultimately, even in our mechanical age—the careful and skilled engine-driver.

one, and in recent years an exhaustive analysis of the real essentials for the safe control of traffic has been undertaken. The results are astonishing, for it turns out that much of the old complexity is quite unnecessary. The prime question to be answered was perfectly clear: what does the man in the signal box really require to know concerning the path to be

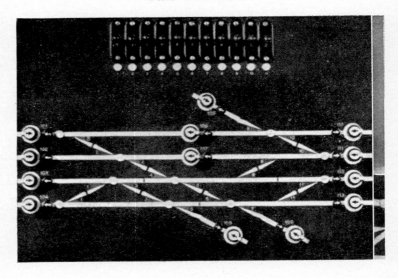

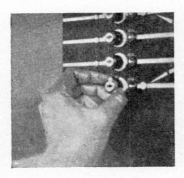
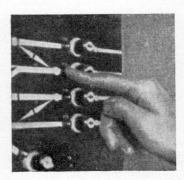

When a train has to be guided through the maze of tracks in a railway station, a number of points (switches) and a multitude of signals have to be operated to lay and protect a clear 'path' for the train. The men in the signal-box control all this from a distance, by levers operating each separate pair of points and each individual signal—unless they are fortunate enough to have the ingeniously simple 'In-Out' system of traffic control. See the text.

prepared for a train? The answer received was equally simple: he needs to know only where the train path is to *start* and where it is to *finish*. In other words, he must know by what track or 'road' the train will enter the area, and along what road it will leave (or where it will come to a final stop, as in the 'dead-ends' of a terminal station).

Readers should suppress their doubts and queries until we can see how this 'In-Out' or NX (*E*ntrance *E*xit) system works.

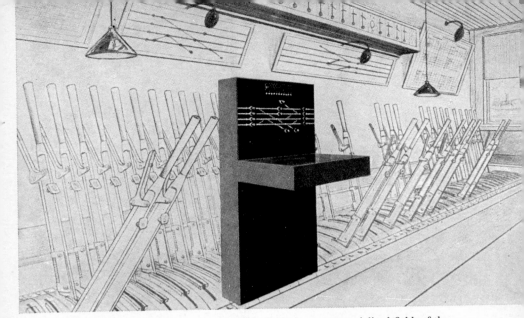

A picture to make one think. It shows a small sample, from a very specialized field, of the implications of technical progress. This is a signal box of the old type: long rows of levers, needing a long pull and a strong pull, to work the rods and wires leading to the points and signals out in the station yard. The little black cabinet in the foreground is all that is left of the old signal box when the new, automatic NX system replaces the pulling of heavy levers by the pressing of small buttons.

The signalman faces a traffic control board (see figure on p. 168) which shows all the lines of rails, or roads, in the station area. At the ends of each road are a pair of push buttons, a large 'IN' (N) button, and a smaller 'Out' (X) button. When the operator now receives notice that a train is approaching, and possibly that it must be brought in on one particular road and brought out along some other particular road, he presses the corresponding N button (bottom left in the figure), and then the appropriate X button (bottom right in the figure). This is literally all he has to do. All the points along the path of the train, from the beginning to the end, are automatically set in their proper positions and locked there. The operator (the successor of the old-time signalman) is informed when this has been done by small lights appearing along the 'train path'. All the signals are automatically cleared along the path and set to 'red' for crossing paths. This too is indicated to the man in the box by a lighted arrow appearing on the N button. The road is now set, and as the train advances through the station area, small sections light up along the control panel, in step with it. A glance at the panel shows the signalman where any train is, at any instant.

Truly an amazing device! No more 'pulling off' of numbers of separate points and signals. All the hundreds of signal levers and the many track diagrams seen, for instance, in the Rome signal box have,

In a marshalling yard, where trains are made up and sorted out again into their component vehicles, there are no regular, timetable movements: trains run to and fro, trucks and carriages are attached and detached, shunted to other lines; new trucks arrive and are sent away elsewhere. Instead of numbers of men, running to and fro, operating points and setting signals by hand, this British Railways marshalling yard has a centralized, remote control over all shunting movements; one man in the cabin controls all points and signals in the yard by the buttons and levers on his 'dashboard'.

by drastic simplification, been reduced to a control panel which is itself a track diagram, and carries only one 'N' and one 'X' button for each train path. It is not surprising that this NX system, developed by the General Railway Signal Company, has been adopted at a number of the world's greatest railway termini, including the Grand Central in New York, Victoria in London, Montreal in Canada, and Adelaide in Australia.

It is both instructive and fascinating to trace such a development from its first origins in an ingenious, promising and extremely simple, fundamental idea, to its realization in the compact piece of apparatus shown on the previous page, so pointedly displaying its superiority over the background of obsolete, clumsy machinery it has displaced.

The engine-driver still watches the signal arms, standing stiffly out from their posts for 'Danger', and slanting upwards (or downwards) for 'Line Clear', or at the many different types of colour signals. These last are coming into fashion increasingly for daytime as well as night use, in the interests of uniformity and standardization of the whole system. The multitude of signals used can be clearly seen from the railways' official books of signal rules and regulations. All these various

At first sight, quite an ordinary photograph of a railway accident. It shows, however, a relatively rare occurrence—a pure locomotive accident: this 'light' engine, running alone, suddenly left the rails and 'ditched'.

types of signals must of course be familiar to the engine-driver, to enable him to act promptly and correctly.

The signals staff on their side, however, also have the duty of simplifying and easing his task as far as possible. Selection of the various types of equipment therefore must be based on careful and thorough research, covering also psychological factors. In this regard, too, the constantly increasing train speeds have played a great part. Consider, for instance, a danger signal. This requires the train to stop *before* reaching the signal. A modern express train, however, must start to brake about a thousand yards before the point at which it finally comes to rest. At such long distances, it may be difficult or even impossible to read the signal. Hence 'advance' or 'distant' signals are used, erected up to ¾-mile in front of the real, or 'home' signal. On some Continental railways, these advance signals are given by round discs at eye height: for 'Stop' the disc is raised and shows its full face to the train; for 'Go' the disc is set 'on edge' and shows only as a thin line. Even this arrangement has proved inadequate at very high speeds. To warn the engine-driver of approach to a 'distant' signal, even further 'advance' signals are sometimes placed ahead of the disc signal.

It is one thing, however, to set a signal to danger and quite another to have the train come to a stop. It requires full and effective control to stop a long and heavy train rushing forward at over 90 m.p.h. The brakes are therefore a very important part of train equipment, and their design and construction an equally important problem of railway engineering. It is not enough to release the speed demons on the line: these forces must be controlled and fettered as and when necessary.

The old 'brake van', just behind the engine or at the tail of the train, or both, is a survival from the first days of railways when it actually was a van with a hand-brake. Obviously, however, when it becomes necessary to stop a train within a reasonably short distance all the locomotive wheels, and all the trucks and carriages must have brakes. The only problem is how to operate them all at once. The first step was to fit a brake on each vehicle, but these brakes could only be operated at the stations. Such a system was then used for goods traffic. If the gradient between two stations rises and falls, the brakes should be set for the 'down grade', with the uncomfortable result that the engine would have to pull the train uphill against the brakes.

An improvement on this method was the provision of hand-brakes on 'brake vans' distributed at short intervals along the train. On a whistle from the engine the 'brakemen' then set the hand-brakes, running along the train from one to the other. On many British slow freight trains it is still the case that when they are running the only brakes that can be operated are those on the engine and on the rear brake van. Other trains are fitted with 'continuous' brakes operated from the engine. Of these, only the various forms of 'air brakes'—pressure or vacuum—remain in current use today.

The first air brakes, introduced in about 1865, were arranged as follows. The locomotive is equipped with a compressed-air container or cylinder. To brake the train, the driver turns a brake-valve, and admits pressure to the train pipe—an air pipe running the whole length of the train. This causes the brake blocks or brake shoes to be pressed against the wheel tyres. This system, however, proved to have dangerous drawbacks and caused a number of accidents. Firstly, the pressure dropped progressively along the train; and secondly, any leak put the whole system out of action—perhaps at the instant of an emergency. Alternative means were sought and a solution adopted which is often used in safety devices generally. It is inconvenient, but not dangerous, if the brakes come *on* at the wrong time—it is far worse if they do *not* act when required. The solution is, therefore, to have the brakes 'on'

A propaganda picture, for the campaign to make the Westinghouse automatic air brake compulsory on American railways. The campaign was conducted by fiery Lorenzo Coffin, the 'Samuel Plimsoll' of the railways, who for twenty years fought the railway companies and collected statistics of 30,000 avoidable train accidents per annum, with which he bombarded the politicians until in the year of victory, 1893, the American Congress passed a bill, drafted by Coffin himself, making continuous air brakes compulsory on all railways of the United States.

as a general rule, and use the braking mechanism to *release* them when required. The brake shoes are kept pressed against the wheels by strong springs; when compressed air is applied, the brake shoes are forced away from the wheels, against the action of the springs. To apply the brakes, therefore, it is only necessary to open the train valve, the air escapes from the train pipe, the pressure drops, and the springs press the brake shoes back against the wheel tyres. The advantage of this arrangement is that, in case of a leak in the system, the air escapes and the train is braked. While it is undesirable to have trains stop at random, it is better that a train should stop when anything goes wrong with the brakes. This simple but extremely effective method was devised by George Westinghouse in 1875 and led to the introduction of automatic braking on railway trains.

Above, we have described a system in which a *higher* pressure is used to keep the brake shoes away from the wheels. It is quite possible, of course, to reverse the arrangement and have the brake shoes pulled away from the wheels by the action of a *vacuum*. In this system, opening the train valve allows air to flow into the empty (exhausted) train pipe. When the suction ceases, the springs press the shoes on to the wheels.

The Westinghouse system has many advantages, but if braking is effected by letting the outside air into the train pipe, every cock and valve in the line can act as an emergency brake. When the 'communication cord' is pulled, air is let into the pipe, and every brake on the train is applied. This arrangement also ensures that, should carriages become detached from the train and continue running under their own impetus, they become automatically braked themselves, and at the same time the brakes are applied on the rest of the train.

'The detective on the trail'—thus we could describe this inspection saloon, which contains a detecting instrument, recording on a paper strip all irregularities or flaws in the rails, as the wheels run over them. The recorded trace also shows the equally-spaced 'ticks' produced by the jolts at the rail joints.

As soon as the instrument shown in the previous illustration has located a fault in a rail, the inspection coach stops. The defective spot is examined by experts, and marked by a symbol on the rail flange for the instruction of the permanent way men or gangers who follow.

It may be asked, why should any accidents occur on a modern railway with all its safeguards? No system, however perfect, is without the possibility of faults and failures at the human end—ultimately, it is the human element which is in control. Most of the human actions involved are safeguarded by control devices, and these by further controls, but somewhere this chain of protection has an end, for any practicable system must be made more or less elastic to allow for unforeseen eventualities. In other words, rules and regulations, however detailed, cannot cover every contingency. Railway regulations acknowledge this, laying down that all signals must be obeyed forthwith and absolutely, unless the recipient has reason to believe that this will

Another type of detector, the Hallade recorder, is used to detect irregularities in the vertical or horizontal straightness of the track which lead to undue oscillation of the coaches at speed. On the Western Region of British Railways this instrument is carried in a special 'whitewash coach', so-called because a splash of white paint for identification purposes, is dropped on every stretch of track which the recorder shows to require attention.

endanger the traffic. And further, that should the giving of a signal involve danger to traffic, such signal shall not be given, excepting to avert a still greater danger. It is well to rely on human brains and judgment in the last resort.

But, however excellent the human brains concerned—and the best are just good enough for this purpose—human attention and speed of reaction have also to be considered. British Railways have over 275,000 separate railway signals. It is not easily possible to say how many times a day these signals are operated: in any event, the number of warnings sent out is by no means small. Men give these many millions of signals, and men have to observe them: not merely hear, see and understand them, but finally to take *action*.

A fairly simple method of warning an engine-driver, possibly automatically, to stop his train at a danger signal. The swinging arm high on the left of the picture follows all the motions of a signal arm farther down the line. At 'danger', the lever lies horizontally. The contact shoe on the tip of the arm then slides over the contact bow visible on the top of the engine. An automatic electric mechanism does the rest; a bell rings and if that escapes the attention of the driver, things come to a stop even without his assistance.

This, obviously, is the weak link in the chain. The man in the signal box does not stop the train—he merely signals it to stop. The modern locomotive may be an engineering wonder, but it is not so wonderful as to be able to stop on a danger signal. It happens, now and again, that a train stands in a station, properly guarded by a danger signal on the line behind it. An express train approaches at speed, over-runs the signal, and causes a bad accident. Occasionally, and miracu-lously, the engine-driver survives. His first words are: "I saw the signal at red, but I could not stop in time." That is the truthful, very human confession of an honest man. That driver had a long and tiring run behind him; he had guided the express with skill and safety over many miles of track. He had passed, seen and obeyed, hundreds of signals. The last signal, just at the journey's end, he also *saw*, but something failed in his bodily reaction to it—he did not *act*.

Automatic devices can come to the aid of the human mechanism of reaction, which is the weak link in the chain of safeguards. The principle is in any case sufficiently simple to allow of many applications. The most obvious idea is to arrange some device which, when a signal moves to danger, makes contact with some part of the locomotive and gives audible warning to the engine-driver. It is simple enough to think of such an arrangement but the difficulty begins in the practical realization—how to obtain reliable and trouble-free action without too much complication and expense.

This conception of a purely mechanical contact releasing first a warning signal and then an automatic braking device on the train is the main feature of the German Kofer system, a picture of which is shown on the previous page. In this, a lever released when the signal is at danger makes contact with the roof of the driver's cab on the engine. In another system, the same result is obtained by a contact block between the rails; when the signal is at danger the block rises and makes contact under the locomotive.

Such devices are rather rough in action when a train is running fast. There are, however, even more ingenious ways of getting the same result; for instance, a beam of light falling on a receiving 'eye' in the locomotive. Electricity can also be used to help in many other ways. This has already been mentioned in describing electric locomotives, which have all facilities for causing an electric warning to be given when a danger signal is overlooked. It is, of course, possible on steam-operated and other non-electrified railways to incorporate electrical instruments of such kind that the locomotive receives an electric impulse when necessary. When such an automatic device is used to intervene where human alertness fails, it is usually necessary to arrange for it to apply the brakes as well. The driver is given a chance first; a bell or a hooter sounds, or a 'Stop' sign lights up before his eyes. If that produces no result, the brakes go on.

But whatever measures are taken, however many safeguards are employed, occasional accidents still do happen. The plain fact is, we shall never attain to a fully-effective guarantee against accidental happenings on a train. With the multitude of trains daily racing along the railway lines of the world, crossing and recrossing in their tracks, driven mercilessly and at top speed past hundreds of thousands of signals and over thousands of points, it would be too much to expect 100 per cent perfection. It must be admitted, however, that railway

A device which acts automatically if the engine driver does not respond to a danger signal. A beam of light from the top of the mast strikes a light-sensitive photoelectric cell, and is aimed exactly at the front rim of the leading wheel of the locomotive. The cell passes an electric current, which is sufficient to sound warning bells or hooters, or, as a last resort, to release a brake on the leading wheels. This appliance is too costly and complicated to be widely used, but deserves mention as an example of the great efforts which are being made to strengthen the weakest link in all systems of safeguards—human fallibility.

signalling safeguards have been brought to an unheard of degree of perfection and reliability, and the millions of railway men—'railway servants'—who have the care of the lives and limbs of their passengers, perform their duties with practically unfailing devotion. Typical statistics for an average year in the present decade, on railways totalling 560,000 miles in length, show that some 2,500 persons may lose their lives in collisions, derailments, and suchlike accidents. The railways themselves suffer most, three-quarters of the victims being railwaymen. These may seem high figures, but it must be remembered that in one average year these railways complete 217,480 *million* passenger-miles. This means that the chance of finding death on the railway occurs once every 373 million miles travelled, per passenger. Travelling steadily at a mile a minute, it would take 700 years for the chance to become a certainty.

By the theory of probability, the chances are 1 in 13 in 700 years, for an individual death. Even in modern, high-comfort trains, no one is likely to test these calculations more thoroughly, but is likely to rely on the chance that 'it can't happen to me'.

CHAPTER VI

COMFORT AND SERVICE

JOURNEY-TIME is a good measure of distance, and we have already discussed in previous pages the interesting question of the significance of speed in railway travel. Some railway time-tables have mileage columns showing distances from the starting-point, but these are seldom used except to calculate a fare—or perhaps to settle a bet. If we are really thinking how 'far' it is from, say, London to Birmingham, we say 'about two hours'; or we may hear the phrase, 'a quarter of an hour less by the express'. We use time as a measure of distance. That is not, however, the subject of this chapter.

What did people take with them in former times, when they made long journeys by stage, mail-coach, or post-chaise? Plenty of clothing—coats, jackets, vests, shawls, rugs and scarves, to pad and protect the body; and food and drink to while away the long hours as they jolted, bounded and swayed about in their clumsy vehicles over the rough roads. All they were concerned with was to keep body and soul reasonably comfortable, to survive the rigours of the journey without too much hardship, and to arrive safely at the other end. Reading, writing, amusement or distraction, such as filled their rainy days or long winter evenings at home, were not to be thought of in a stage coach. A post-chaise, bouncing over potholes or floundering in mud, was no setting for books, paper, pens and ink.

Modern man, travelling by rail, also takes things for the journey, but usually very little. Overcoats are often removed in the carriage. Temperature is controlled by a handle, which can be pushed over from 'cold' to 'hot' and vice-versa. The personal luggage goes in a rack. Our passenger of today then settles down comfortably, with book or paper, pipe or box of sweets. Some travellers like to employ their time usefully, since the hours spent in the compartment must not be wasted. Business must be looked into, or preparations made for the forthcoming

In front of the platform barriers at Roma Termini railway station. When it was completed in 1950, Italy could boast of possessing one of the most handsome and most up-to-date railway stations in the world.

conference. Out come the more or less important 'documents', to be spread over the little table, the fountain-pen comes into play, and in an instant the busy passenger is in spirit in an 'office' which, unheeded by him, is racing forward at many miles an hour.

Having thus visualized the two types of passengers of two different periods—the coach traveller, swathed in top-coats, carried passively on his uncomfortable and often dangerous way, and the modern railway traveller, able to relax and enjoy a good or a busy time according to his inclinations while carried smoothly forward in a comfortable express train—we are not able to appreciate why, in all travelling, time is a measure of distance. If the train covers the distance six times faster than the mail coach, it is surely justifiable to say that the railway has shortened the journey by five-sixths. Strictly speaking, only the time has been reduced to one-sixth; but the passenger appreciates the result in terms of distance for the simple reason that an hour in a jolting coach passes far more tediously—or 'slowly'—than an hour in a fast train.

The practical consequence of this is that most of us would rather spend six hours in a railway train than three in a horse-coach. Thus, the railway virtually 'shortens' the journey to one-twelfth. Not only the speed of the rushing, striving locomotive, but also the comfort of the carriages, help to shorten our journeys.

But let us be fair and not confine ourselves to the purely subjective view. In calculating the time 'spent' on a journey, in addition to the pure running time, we must also consider the fact that eating and sleeping are also activities on which we spend time. In travelling from London to Edinburgh, starting at 10.15 p.m. and arriving at, say 6.0 a.m., I have not 'wasted' seven and three-quarter hours on the run. I have had my night's sleep as well, and while I slept British Railways kindly carried me on to my destination. Properly considered, I have spent 'no' time on the journey. If I had slept at home, I would have got nowhere. Most people do not complain of time 'spent' in sleeping, resting or eating, yet some people do complain of having to 'spend'

These girls have their hands full, attending to place reservations for anything from one to ninety days ahead, in the 54 'limited' trains daily leaving Pennsylvania Station, New York. They sit round nine drums revolving in a central frame, and having in all 43,524 little pigeon holes for different coloured markers. The system works perfectly and prevents two people being put in the same berth. The congestion at this super-railway station is so great, that eleven such machines are needed to keep abreast of all demands for reservations.

long hours getting from one place to another even while sleeping,
resting or eating. They are not realists.

It can be quite fairly said, therefore, that railway journeys are made
less time-wasting, not merely by technical improvements in locomotive
power and traffic control, but equally by the increased comfort in the
passengers' domain—First or Second class, as the case may be.
Consequently, a short chapter on passenger comfort deserves to be
included in a book on the conquest of space and time.

Some people suffer from 'railway fever'. The impatient desire to
quit the carriage at the journey's end, which attacks even fit and
experienced travellers, ensures that no one remains longer than strictly
necessary in the atmosphere of a railway train. The atmosphere of a
railway is, however, undoubtedly characteristic and even exciting,
though best taken in limited doses. No fundamentally unspoiled human
being can feel the atmosphere of a large and busy railway station
without knowing the travel urge, the 'wanderlust' which rises within
him. The indescribable blend of odours and sounds is quite international—a heady cocktail, brewed to exactly the same recipe whether
in New York, Paris, or in our own home station.

While the railway thus wakes our inborn, age-old desires to go out
into the world, to see foreign climes and meet strange people, to experience change, new impressions and adventures, it can also raise hopes

Photograph of a model of the new Central Station at Oslo in Norway: rather more imposing
and commodious than the old one, in which railway staffs for long years struggled and toiled,
with entirely inadequate facilities, to keep traffic moving.

An interior view of a passenger car on the Baltimore and Ohio Railroad, U.S.A., from a sketch made about the middle of the last century. There is little doubt that this car is heated, and the gentleman nearest the stove looks most uncomfortable, even without his coat!

which are not always fulfilled. It must be remembered that the railway is a means of transport, not a magic carpet. It is true that transportation—*i.e.*, being carried from place to place—is the one essential for all travel, but this is only the most prosaic and subordinate part of that whole complex of sensations and experience which can make a journey so delightful. The railway is the specialized means, not the aim and end, of transportation. This task it undertakes with skill and energy, applying the latest technical methods of the machine age. The whole, gigantic transport organization exists to convey the passenger from place to place with a degree of safety, reliability and punctuality hitherto undreamed of, and with a standard of comfort falling short of only the most extreme demands of a spoilt and cosseted travelling public.

These results have not been attained without sacrifices. There is a world of difference between the wayfarer of olden days, toiling on his way, on foot, in the saddle, or by coach along the roads, and the modern railway passenger, demanding from the railway high standards of punctuality and luxurious comfort. This is not, necessarily, all progress. Many a railway passenger, hemmed in by bye-laws, surrounded by public notices of objects and activities forbidden and permitted, confined in the strait-jacket of a mercilessly precise time-table, may spare a wry thought for the free wanderer, pacing the highways and by-ways at will—his own master of every detail of his journey. Weary and sore, he may be, rainsoaked and sunburnt, but he is free. The hills are high and steep, but the view from the summit is rewarding.

The railway does not climb such steep slopes, and where a view appears, the train will quite probably dive hastily away from it into a cutting or a tunnel. In the old days, one 'undertook' journeys, by coach, post-chaise or private carriage. One spent days on the road, and could find travelling both amusing and interesting, and varied by nights at cosy inns. The whole was an experience—'seeing life'—and there was a great deal to relate on arriving at the journey's end. At the present day, about the only experience to relate after crossing the Alps by an international night express is the discomfort of an upper berth.

It is possible thus to romanticize, however, to the detriment of scientific and technical progress, about many more subjects than railway travel. The effective and continuing fulfilment of certain well-defined needs resulting from a mechanized way of life can invariably be obtained by the application of a methodical, standardized technique. If the wants of human beings come within the scope of such mechanical treatment, it is difficult to take account of idiosyncracies and personal preferences. A measure of individual freedom must be sacrificed if advantage is to be taken of modern, technical progress; whether or not the price is too high is a matter for debate.

From the instant the traveller crosses the threshold of the railway station, and up to the moment when he leaves the station at the end of his journey, it is the aim and intention of all concerned to convey him and his luggage as quickly and smoothly as possible through all stages of his peregrinations. Obviously, no such complete mechanization as can be applied in the case of inanimate objects—in a factory production line, for instance—is possible here. It cannot be denied, however, that in some ways and to an appreciable extent this 'ideal' has been very closely approached. The most obvious example is that of large-scale troop-transport by rail. In dealing with the general travelling public a difference arises in that the public is not willing to submit itself to military discipline, and, furthermore, the passengers do not arrive at the railway station already grouped tidily according to trains and destinations. This sorting process must be performed on the station itself.

A 'roomette' on a modern American train by day. Compare with the picture on page 188.

A further drawback is that passengers usually bear no outward and visible sign of their intended destination. It is thus not possible to pass them through any sorting process which could automatically despatch them to the correct trains. The working principle must be that of co-operation, of combined action between the station staff and their dispositions, and the passenger.

This, in fact, can be observed at any busy station. The sorting principle adopted rests on the fair assumption that any passengers able to read clear and simple notices are able to find their own way without troubling the staff with questions. But in practice, this system often seems to break down. Every single railwayman on the platform is constantly bombarded by a flood of more or less absurd and unnecessary inquiries, and neither experience in the art of travelling nor knowledge of the resources of the system appear sufficient to enable the general public to pass through like packages and automatically land in their respective compartments.

There are people who can make this effort, and their number is increasing. These are the expert travellers who arrive the necessary minimum number of minutes before the time of departure, cast a swift glance at the notice boards, go straight to the right ticket window,

A double compartment or 'roomette' on an American train at night.

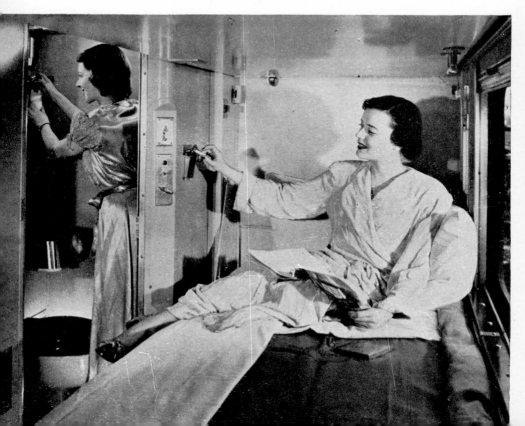

pass through the right doors, make any unavoidable small purchases
swiftly and efficiently, arrive on the right platform, enter the right train
and finally, with a self-satisfied smile, sink down in their allotted place
just as the train begins to move. It is not so long since the country
bumpkin at the ticket-window was a subject for caricaturists. The
average passenger of today occupies a place somewhere between the
two. This average is improving steadily, but from the railwayman's
point of view, there is still much to be done to educate the public in
'travel technique'.

Our present-day, average traveller can read a notice, and can
usually be relied on to find the right hour in a time-table. Old-time
indolence and unreadiness are, however, still well in evidence, and in
the rush of a journey Mr. Traveller loses in part the assurance of the
reasonable being he claims to be. It must be confessed that he does not
always get the meaning of a notice, however boldly printed and simply
worded. If there is a chance to go wrong, or to act foolishly, he is as
likely as not to take it. The ideal railway station, therefore, would be
one where all chances of making mistakes and doing foolish things are
anticipated and eliminated, and to realize such an ideal station is the
aim and endeavour of all railways. The solution of this problem will
depend greatly on the manner of assessing what constitutes an average
traveller, or, more correctly, what minimum of common sense, intelli-
gence, consideration and good humour can be expected of our voyager.
It is not a flattering picture that railwaymen have formed of Mr.
Traveller, who represents all of us at our worst.

He comes racing up at the last minute, is annoyed that the taxi-
driver cannot give change for a note, and wastes no little precious time
making up the correct fare. The large trunk is to be registered. He is most
disturbed that this cannot be done before he has bought his ticket. If he
cannot produce a ticket, he must pay the full, excess freight charge. The
porter, who has seen all this happen before, suggests that Mr. Traveller
should go and buy his ticket while he, the porter, will see to the trunk.
Mr. Traveller rushes to the booking hall and joins the first queue he sees,
and is nearly at bursting point when his turn comes at the window.

"First, single."

"Sorry—Second only—next window on the right!" Mr. Traveller
would have done better to move over quickly to the next window, but
he must stop and argue the point, and express himself freely about the
way things are managed. The booking clerk remains unimpressed. At
the next window, fortunately, things go well, and he gets his little bit
of pasteboard. Now back to the luggage counter, where he finds neither
trunk nor porter. Loud complaints to a railway official standing by.

As feared, our Mr. Traveller is too late. Even if, after his mighty struggles, he had the energy for a Bannister-like spurt, he would still miss his train. Mr. Traveller might even have made it in the end—if it had not been for that fussy guard—who was only doing his duty.

"What was the porter's number?"

"How should *I* know?"

"Where are you going?"

"What's *that* got to do with it?"

"Nothing—but this counter is for Northbound traffic only, and. . . ."

A quick dash to the right counter, and he finds both trunk and porter. One more difficulty—it is three minutes to train departure-time, and registered luggage for this train is only accepted up to ten minutes before. More explosions, during which the unruffled porter gets the trunk away to the train on one of those busy little electric battery trucks. At the gate, Mr. Traveller thrusts his ticket at the first ticket inspector he meets.

"Number 6 please!"

"Why couldn't you say so before?"

The inspector could have pointed out that the train-times and destinations are shown in bright, illuminated letters over all the gates, but he has other things to do. At last, Mr. Traveller lands on the right platform and sees his trunk just going into the van. Maybe it is too much to hope that a thought of gratitude will flit through his mind as he sees this example of the helpfulness of an organization he has just been bitterly reviling, and appreciates how easy it would have been for the attendants to stand by the regulations and not made the extra effort to help him.

In any case, our Mr. Traveller jumps on his train, finds he is in a third-class carriage, pushes his way through corridors blocked with standing passengers (he could just as easily have first looked from the platform to see where the first-class carriages were standing) and at last finds the right class. All full, unfortunately; all seats taken, except that nice one in the corner, into which he sinks with relief.

Unfortunately, here comes another Mr. Traveller: "Sorry, my seat!" Expostulations and arguments from Mr. Traveller No. 1. "No luggage . . . not occupied . . . etc., etc." Mr. Traveller No. 2 waves a reservation slip at him. "Sorry!" The guard, hearing the altercation, comes along to settle the matter. Those who have taken the trouble to reserve their seats beforehand must have priority. Furthermore, this particular carriage is not—repeat *not*—going to our Mr. Traveller's destination. How was *he* to know? It says so, on a nice, large destination board on the outside of the carriage! If only he had taken a good look from the platform, before boarding the train! However, the guard finds Mr. Traveller No. 1 a seat also; the train is now about ready to pull out.

Here comes Traveller No. 3, hot and breathless. "Poor old mother . . . due any minute . . . can the train wait?" It cannot—the time-table

One of the new 'armchair specials' of the Norwegian State Railways. The seats are adjustable, and can be tilted backwards for comfortable sleeping at night.

A stainless-steel kitchen on a modern American express train.

must be followed to the second. The guard's whistle blows, the green flag waves, and the train at last puffs out.

It may be thought that we have painted too gloomy a picture of what might happen. Such an unadulterated example of stupidity and irritability can hardly be accepted as the norm. But our quite impossible 'Mr. Traveller' does unite in his person all the faults and failings which are in daily evidence (in more diluted versions, it is true) on the railways. The railway authorities, therefore, have to adopt their organization for handling passengers to the level of these bottom-of-the-class cases. A whole science of 'passenger psychology' has thus been developed by railway administrations.

Even the simple matter of notice boards, indicators and their correct placing is a problem in itself. Considerable knowledge of human psychology is involved. Notice boards have to be placed so that the prospective passenger is 'painlessly' guided from point to point, in the correct sequence, and in the shortest time possible. We cannot but admit that the desired goal has been approached remarkably closely, although occasionally passengers still manage to misuse even the most fool-proof system.

Another problem arising in regard to this matter of organization is the extent to which it is possible to rely on the common sense and individual co-operation of the passengers. This is a very important point, the solution of which is by no means automatic but requires prolonged consideration.

As a concrete example, let us take the handling of passenger's luggage. In many countries this is handed in by the passenger against a receipt, or 'check'. On presentation of this check, the luggage is delivered back to the owner. There are, however, other ways of ensuring that trunks and bags do not get into the wrong hands. In Britain, for instance, the luggage is loaded in the van, duly labelled and arranged according to destination. At each station the corresponding packages are unloaded on to the platform, where they are claimed by the passengers, who identify their own belongings. The porter picks up the bags indicated and carries them out—without any other uniformed official intervening. Theoretically, this seems a hopelessly and helplessly naïve solution to all those 'experts' in human nature, but, in point of fact, it works well. Self-service is an astoundingly simple solution, and it is often the most successful.

Simple and time-saving solutions are urgently called for when we consider the masses of passengers handled by any really big railway station. Paris stations handle about 1,000,000 passengers daily in suburban traffic alone. One single station, Gare Saint-Lazare, des-

M

A rear-end observation car on the Baltimore & Ohio Railway. Note the lack of formality in the arrangement of the comfortable chairs and tables, and the provision for family groups or friends to sit together. Note also the large windows giving an uninterrupted view.

patches 50,000 passengers between 6.15 and 7.15 p.m.—over 800 per minute! The relatively small proportion of suburban traffic passing through this station requires nearly a thousand trains each day; in the rush hours there is approximately one departure a minute. In addition, there are all the long-distance trains, most of which have to run over the same tracks. As these expresses approach the capital from all directions they enter the suburban traffic zone while they are still about thirty miles out. Obviously, these fliers cannot be expected to reduce speed to the leisurely pace of the local trains. The track must be cleared for them and the 'locals' must give way.

At Havre and Cherbourg, special expresses wait to take the passengers from the giant Atlantic liners. If these are a little late, all the traffic suffers—not only the expresses but even the suburban locals in and out of Paris, which have to keep 'line clear' longer than would otherwise be necessary. Thousands of passengers stand waiting at the small suburban stations, grumbling and complaining about the stupendous inefficiency of the railway authorities, who cannot even

keep the local trains running punctually. It is hardly reasonable to
expect the small-town suburban passenger to realize that a fog-bank
in mid-Atlantic has caused his 'local' to be delayed for so many minutes.

But in spite of our 'Mr. Traveller', in spite of his old mother, in
spite of all the other good and sufficient reasons for delaying a train—
just one minute, just two minutes, just ten minutes—on the whole the
trains continue to leave the stations 'on the dot'. Let us take a glance
at the tremendous work required to accomplish this miracle—or rather,
series of miracles—day in and day out. We start from the entirely
concrete assumption that the train is ready alongside the platform,
dead on time, correctly made up, with full train crew and equipment,
engine ready to start, carriages clean, washed and in order, and 'all
aboard' for the start.

The careful planning which has brought matters to this stage is
not our business at the moment: the necessary calculations and considerations have already been made and taken in the railway offices
on the basis of comprehensive statistical data, reports and memoranda
from interested parties—areas—business circles—tourist and travel
agencies. The activities we are now about to describe are those concerned with the regions outside the station area 'down the line'.

In a previous chapter, we have already gained an impression of
the imposing technical progress embodied in the modern, giant railway
locomotives. We shall now take a glance at the work done out on the

Any self-respecting, modern, long-distance train (in America—of course) must have its
'picture theatre'. You press a button—and are provided with ten minutes of relaxation,
with up-to-date news reels, or features, as the case may be.

The mails are important, but the express can hardly be expected to stop for a single mailbag. At full speed, the bag is dropped into the net waiting at the station. Quite a series of experiments was needed to find a sufficiently reliable and responsive mechanism to allow this to be done at a train speed of 60–90 m.p.h. At such speeds, even an ordinary mailbag becomes something of a projectile.

lines by the smaller (and even the smallest) locomotives, the shunting engines and the like. They can draw long lines—the railwayman calls them 'rakes'—of empty carriages nearly as well as the giants of the open road, 'spotting' them with precision through the tangle of lines in the station yards, where track ranges next to track, and a multitude of points and signals lurk for the unwary. Out from the gloom of the station roof the shunting engine steams proudly, dragging its long line of trucks and carriages with all the importance of a main-line engine. The shunters are perched on steps and footboards, experts in their own intricate tasks which are not always particularly safe. The shunting engine backs carefully on to the train, the shunter nips between the buffers and 'hooks on', swiftly and deftly. A wave of the arm, a whistle, and the line of vehicles rattles forward over many, many points, out to the 'carriage sidings' which are the trains' waiting-room. Here come the trains which have just emptied all their passengers out on to the busy platforms, and here they are made ready again to take on a new load.

The first job for the shunting engine after delivering the empty 'rake' to the carriage sidings, is to detach the mail-vans, since the paper 'passengers' are in just as great a hurry as the human contingent. The former go to the 'Post-Office' platforms, where the staff are already waiting to fall on the mail bags, sort them out and send them on.

The remaining carriages stand waiting, and appear to be badly in need of a wash and brush-up, after the rigours of the long journey. It is not only the external dirt, soot and cinders, often streaked and stained with rain water, which must be cleaned off. 'Interior cleanliness' is even more important. It is unbelievable what some people, in some countries, will leave behind them in a railway carriage. There are countries where it is quite useless to provide ashtrays, since passengers deliberately prefer to throw their ashes and cigarette-ends straight on to the floor—in all classes, first or otherwise. People behave in railway carriages as they would never think of behaving in their own homes.

This is a genuine photograph of a railway compartment in the state in which it was left by some holiday travellers. No doubt they were on their worst behaviour, but there is little excuse for treating public vehicles in such a manner in any circumstances.

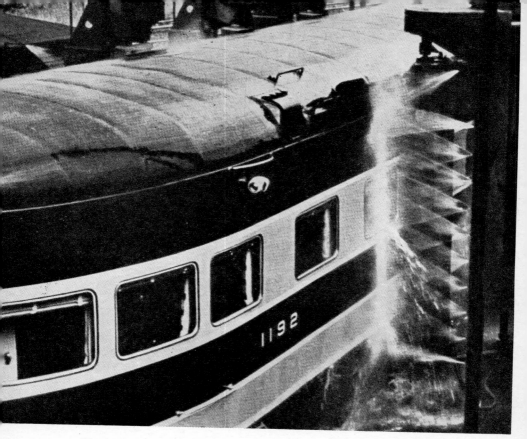

The 'streamliner' has a wash and brush-up, while slowly passing under an array of sprays and brushes in a modern automatic carriage-washing plant . . . .

A large proportion of the travelling public appear almost to take pride in behaving as badly as possible, where the risk of detection is so slight. Normally well behaved at home, people wipe dirty knives on tablecloths and towels, or curtains, and placidly let cigarette ends burn large holes through carpets and upholstery. One's faith in the essential decency of ordinary people receives a rude shock at the sight of the misuse to which railway equipment is subjected in passenger trains. The authorities have required to develop considerable ingenuity in devising automatic containers for soap, towels and drinking cups, which are both fool-proof and hygienic, and to arrange toilets and similar accommodation so as to give the travelling public the least scope for soiling and destroying them. But there are always the untameable few. Railwaymen are not, however, unduly pessimistic. Experience has shown that the public can be educated, and that the part played by the railways in teaching good manners is not as small as might be expected.

... and now it is the turn of the windows, which receive their beauty-treatment as the scrubber passes over them.

Tucked away among the carriage sidings is a small, corrugated iron hut—the office of the yard foreman. He is the head of the large staff of carriage cleaners who take over the arriving 'empties'. Hardly has a train stopped before they start work, with brooms, brushes and vacuum cleaners, hoses and buckets of soapy water—all equipment specially selected in the light of long experience on the railways. All doors are opened wide, all windows let right down, and soon a flow of old newspapers, empty bottles, orange peel, corks, cigarette ends and other rubbish pours like an avalanche out of the doors, followed by thick clouds of dust. This disposes of all the things people have deliberately jettisoned.

Handkerchiefs, walking-sticks, umbrellas, handbags, brief-cases, books, pipes, cameras and the like have already been collected earlier, labelled with train, carriage and compartment number, and the date, and taken to the lost-property office. It is quite incredible, the things that people forget. A large station can collect in its lost property office

anything up to 600 umbrellas—and half a dozen complete dentures—
annually. When we realize, however, that passengers leave behind
them wooden legs and, as actually happened in one occasion, an
artificial arm with the day's paper still gripped in the wooden hand,
we can well imagine that lost-property staff begin to develop a sound
sense of humour and a philosophy all their own.

Meanwhile, the battle against dust and dirt continues with
undiminished vigour—mechanized as far as possible. The ordinary,
homely vacuum cleaner is inadequate in such conditions. The larger
railway centres have whole 'exhauster' systems to which suction pipes
can be connected where convenient. When all the inside has been
thoroughly cleaned and put in order, all doors and windows are firmly
closed, and the carriages are run slowly under sets of water sprays and
scrubbing brushes. Such a machine consists of vertical rollers carrying
long whisks of cotton waste. These are rotated rapidly while the carriage
passes through, and removes every speck of dirt from the outside of
the carriage with uncanny facility.

The next operation is to polish the windows brightly, inside and
out, and also the notice-boards, destination boards, raised lettering,
fittings and door handles, until all begin to shine and gleam with the
desired sparkle. Now the carriage passes along rails over an inspection
pit. The pit is equipped with powerful electric lights and contains
various mechanical appliances for cleaning and repairing all the
underframe and equipment. Bearings and brakes, pipe-lines, electric
batteries and gas-cylinders are overhauled and renewed, and grease
boxes are filled up. At the same time, the cabinets at the ends
of the carriage are supplied with fresh water, clean water-bottles,
glasses, etc. Experts check over the emergency brakes and heating
regulators.

After all this work has been done, the carriage is at last washed
and clean and ready for service—unless the foreman has noticed anything wrong while making his tour of inspection and has had the
carriage withdrawn from the train-set. Perhaps a cushion-cover has
split—then back goes the carriage to the upholstery-shop. It may even
happen that the foreman's keen eye has observed some of those unpleasant little insects 'forgotten' by a passenger. Or the foreman may
receive a telephone message from one of the stations on the line,
reporting a suspected case of infectious disease among the passengers
on that particular run. Both parasites and microbes give extra work to
the yard engine, which must cut out the particular carriage from its
'rake' and replace it by a spare one. The shunting engine puffs away
with the errant carriage to the disinfecting station, a miniature tunnel-

section which can be sealed airtight. In this tunnel the air is pumped out and formaldehyde vapour or other disinfectant is pumped in.

Meanwhile, the yard engine is still busy, panting to and fro, pulling and hauling until it has 'made up the set', with long, sleek, polished vehicles in the middle—the restaurant cars. Alert men flit swiftly from carriage to carriage, checking couplings, connecting brake-pipes, lowering the gangway plates and coupling up the bellows-curtains.

All trains are made up to a fixed plan and routine, and in accordance with strict rules. Thus, for example, trains are limited according to their speed to a certain number of vehicles, expressed in terms of tonnage. Further rules govern the total length of a train, according to the lines over which it is to run. The majority of the expresses have a 'fixed set' of carriages, running through from end to end of the journey, and extra carriages are attached or detached *en route*, possibly from or to other trains, proceeding in other directions. To prevent tedious shunting at way-stations or junctions, the vehicles in a train set are arranged in such order that only the foremost or rearmost carriage or carriages need be shunted. Strict rules are laid down for the type of

The 'Golden Arrow' steams out from Victoria Station, in London, on its way to Dover for France and beyond. The name on the front of the engine and the great gilt arrows leave the public in no doubt as to what train this is.

vehicle to be run in each train, the number of smoking and non-smoking compartments, the number of seats of each class. These regulations, which are of course subject to variation from time to time, are laid down on the basis of extensive and detailed traffic statistics. A collection of vehicles such as run to and fro regularly between two terminal stations in a scheduled train form a train set. Several such sets are used for the *Flying Scotsman*, the *Golden Arrow*, the *Irish Mail*, etc., and run continually between their two end-points. Additional units may be put on or taken off, but the basic set remains the same.

When a train has been 'made up' in this fashion, a special inspector checks whether all is in order and according to regulations. His duty is also to attach the 'destination boards' on the carriages. He may stop abruptly in the midst of this task, and refer to his list. He has found at

The 'Broadway Limited' runs between the three largest cities in the United States, New York, Philadelphia and Chicago, and is a train which gives the most convincing proof of the revolution which has taken place in American railway services. The luxury and elegance of the exterior of these electric streamliners have already been seen (p. 130). This is a picture of one of the 'little snuggeries' on the train: a cosy compartment with a private wireless, two good beds which fold back into the wall in the daytime, bath and shower, and two roomy hanging cupboards. This is more than any road or air transport can yet offer.

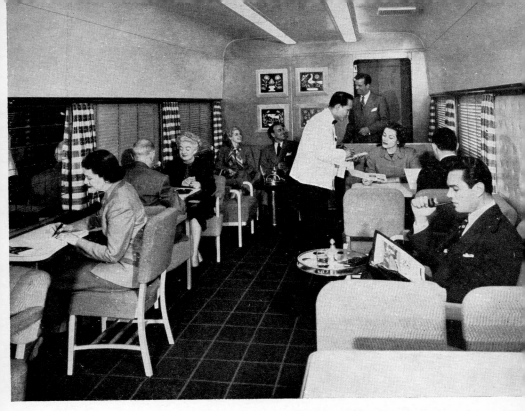

The 'Broadway Limited' can also show other interior arrangements making for quiet and restful travelling: reading on comfortable settees, a hand at bridge at a comfortable table, a little letter-writing at a convenient desk, or some refreshment in good, congenial company.

the last moment some defect in a carriage which makes it inadvisable for that vehicle to be allowed to run in the train in which it has been marshalled. So this carriage must be replaced by a spare. Each railway vehicle has its running number and is assigned to a particular depot. The system is so complete that the head office can tell at any time where each vehicle is—or should be. A 'running schedule' is drawn up, in order to make the fullest use of all rolling stock and to ensure that the minimum number of vehicles only remain idle at any one moment. The arrangement of these schedules requires great ingenuity and accuracy and involves a great deal of work.

In countries with a large and widely branching railway network a considerable office staff is required, to set up and supervise the running schedules. In joint traffic over land frontiers between neighbouring countries, rolling stock often travels long distances over 'foreign' lines. For this system to work satisfactorily, strict observance of the many provisions contained in regulations and agreements is necessary. Foreign trucks may occasionally be seen at stations labelled in various ways, such as "Return to . . .", "Immediate Return to . . .", "To . . . only", and so forth. These are reminders to the railway in regard to other railways' rolling-stock.

In cold weather, most passenger and some freight rolling stock can be heated by special steam pipes out in the yards, with a view to saving locomotive steam. The train engine is usually coupled on at the last possible moment, to economize supplies of coal and water in the tender. But, winter and summer, there is much to do before the passengers can be admitted. Each train guard and attendant checks to see that everything is in order in the carriages for which he is responsible, and looks over his reservation lists, labelling the places accordingly. A woman inspector checks the toilets. Finally, the little shunting engine again arrives and hauls the whole train out to the right platform under the big station roof.

The train engine now backs down from the engine shed (sometimes called the 'round house') which may be situated a mile or so from the terminal station. The big engine glides smoothly up to the train and the couplings are made fast. The brake-pump is started and when the pressure has risen the brake valves are 'cracked open'. Loud hisses from carriage to carriage indicate that the brakes are being tested.

Once upon a time, this was the height of elegance on the railway. A carriage of the International Sleeping Car Company, some seventy years ago—with passengers of the period.

Steam-heating pipes are also coupled up to the engine and the train becomes a living, organized entity.

A last signal lights up ahead; the engine driver makes a quick last test of the brakes—on, off, the bustle on the platform increases, late-arriving 'Mr. Travellers' (Mrs. and Misses, too) storm the platform gates. The guard looks at his watch, then at the station clock. The last doors bang, the last farewells are called. "Stand back there!" A whistle —a wave of the guard's flag—and, right on the second—"She's off!"

The modern railway carriage is undoubtedly the most comfortable vehicle ever placed at the disposal of the travelling public the whole world over. The railway carriage has undergone the same tremendous development as the railway locomotive. Originally only the flanged wheels and somewhat primitive coupling arrangements distinguished it from any other four-wheeled road vehicle. If built quite short, in fact, railway carriages could be built on an even more simple model than road coaches. The swivelling front wheels could be replaced by a fixed axle. However, as railway carriages grew in size—that is to say, in length—it became necessary to give the wheels some freedom of motion with regard to the carriage body. Two stages in development, two steps in progress, then followed, one on the heels of the other.

'Emigrant class' in the eighties of the last century travelled in rougher style. However, the practical 'bunks' for the small travelling folk might serve a useful purpose, even today.

The rush hours, morning and evening, confront modern suburban traffic managers with an enormous and almost overwhelming problem, which the Long Island Railroad in the United States, for instance, has endeavoured to solve by seating the passengers in two storeys, thus accommodating 134 per carriage instead of 80. Such a 'two-decker' costs up to £40,000.

Even before the age of scientific wonders means existed for talking with a bright young lady in the next room; particularly if there was a hole in the wall. This earnest citizen, however, is not talking with the lady. He is an American business man, talking from the train with any subscriber he wishes, by radio telephony, through an ordinary telephone exchange and the usual wire system.

First came the use of springs, to damp down the vibrations from the track before they reached the carriage body. These enabled the carriages to run in a smooth and easy fashion, hitherto undreamt-of, while at the same time resistance in curves was considerably reduced. The next step was to assemble all the necessary pairs of wheels in two 'trucks' or 'bogies'. A modern railway carriage has such a bogie at each end, each with from four to six wheels. The bogies are rotatable, and also able to move sideways within limits. In such a modern bogie carriage the swing of the two ends is to some extent in balance. Seasoned travellers prefer a sleeping compartment in the middle of the carriage.

One of the most uncomfortable features of travelling in the old-time railway carriages was the continual bumping and clashing of the couplings. Elastic couplings and spring buffers are now used, to soften these shocks. European railways normally use a pair of buffers at each end, while the American carriages have a single one on the centre-line. By standing on the platform or by the side of the line, and watching

The principal feature of the new American passenger trains is the tasteful arrangement and practical, solid comfort. They are far removed from the pompous luxury of the millionaires' saloon cars of former days, with their 'bridal suites'. The trains are composed of two classes, 'coach,' and 'Pullman' (the latter at a supplementary fare), and have to compete with road and air services; they have one luxury feature which their competitors for the public favour lack—roominess.

the buffers and couplings at work, we can gain some idea of how these mighty springs 'give and take' as easily and smoothly as the springs in a mattress.

In the earliest days of rail travel, passengers sat in open trucks on cross-benches which had no backs or arm-rests. When important people travelled they hired a goods truck, loaded the family coach on it, maids and footmen sitting in the boot and on the box, and so rode in comfort. Travelling in open trucks was no great pleasure. True, it was a great event, indeed a wonderful adventure, to travel behind the new 'iron horse', but this same 'horse' could damp enthusiasm very effectively by blackening the passengers' faces and spoiling the ladies' finery—obviously displayed in honour of the great occasion. Red-hot cinders pouring so busily out of the chimney occasionally even set fire to passengers' luggage. It became fashionable, therefore, to travel with umbrellas; if that was considered insufficient protection, face-masks and goggles were on sale.

It was soon obvious that open carriages were unsuitable for steam railways. George Stephenson used closed carriages, modelled on the

A Pullman luxury coach as used in the 'Golden Arrow'. The Pullman Car Company Limited, of England, has, however, no connection with the American firm of Pullman which was founded by George Mortimer Pullman as the Pullman Palace Car Company, of Chicago, in 1867. The English company runs 208 cars on the Southern, Western, Eastern, North Eastern and Scottish Regions of British Railways. The average weight of a Pullman, is 40 tons, each first-class coach carrying from 20 to 26 passengers, and each third-class from 32 to 42 passengers.

mail and stage coaches of his day. Gradually the carriages became larger and, in Europe at least, were divided into compartments with separate side-doors. The modern system (used on the continent) with end-doors only, and a through gangway or corridor, comes from America. America, too, introduced upholstered seats and lavatories. The appearance of these improvements was probably due to the severe competition experienced from the river steamers which, by the standards of the day, offered a degree of comfort approaching luxury.

The great name in railway carriage building is George M. Pullman, who invented the first real sleeping-car in 1864. In the daytime it was arranged as a 'saloon', but at night the backs of the seats lifted up and berths were formed in two storeys. The 'dining-car' he inaugurated three years later attracted possibly even more attention. In 1887 Pullman achieved his life's ambition—a complete luxury train, made up of saloon-cars, dining- and sleeping-cars, all with internal corridors and enclosed gangways between the vehicles. This arrangement was most suitable for long journeys, and the *'trains de luxe'* which now run on the great transcontinental railways and the European international trunk lines have reached a standard of comfort very near to perfection. The amenities offered equal those of a modern hotel, and include a bar, reading-room, library, hairdressing saloon and even baths. A few pleasures, such as billiards and table tennis, are still lacking but they may yet come! Telephones, wireless and the cinema are already almost commonplace.

We should not, however, measure the improvement in railway passengers' comfort merely by the more or less superfluous luxury of the 'first-class only' trains, with 'Pullman supplement'. Fortunately it can also be truly claimed that, even for the ordinary passenger, a more

N

comfortable journey has been made possible by improvements in such fundamentals as carriage-construction, heating, lighting and ventilation, and—last, but not least—hygiene. The first candles on spikes fixed to the wall, and the first coal stoves in the cars, probably excited the same admiration in their day as is now evoked by the up-to-date strip-lighting and electric panel-heating of modern trains.

All important trains make extensive use of electricity. On electric railways this is the obvious solution, and on steam-hauled trains a turbo-generator set on the engine, or small generators driven off the carriage axles, provide current. Alternatively, storage batteries can be used and re-charged at terminal stations. However, although electric light would appear from all aspects to be preferable, gas, in special forms, remains a serious competitor in a few countries. That is due to the Swede, Dalen, who invented the AGA light. By a simple and ingenious arrangement, sufficient quantities of acetylene gas can be carried in steel bottles, which are exchanged at main stations. This method of train lighting is so simple, cheap and efficient that only the safety aspect prevents its wide adoption; the gas bottles are, however, liable to explode in train accidents.

Train heating has developed with the same rapidity. Stoves in the carriages were superseded by heaters under the carriage floor. These needed attention and adjustment at way-stations. The handles with the tempting 'Hot' and 'Cold' labels could, however, prove misleading, as many old travellers on Norwegian railways at 'forty below' may recall. When the fire died down, which did sometimes happen, the regulator handle at 'Hot' might still give the impression of warmth, but the icicles on the window-panes were more convincing proof to the contrary. Regulation was usually possible from outside the carriage. If the regulator had already been put full over to 'Hot', however, in

The 'Train of Tomorrow', designed and built by General Motors and sent out on demonstration runs over the United States to publicize all the new ideas incorporated in this paradise on wheels for the traveller. One of the new features shown in the photograph is the so-called 'dome car'. This hood of heat and light-proof plastic, giving a lofty and unbroken view of the countryside, is only one of the many tempting innovations offered by the railways in competing against air and road transport.

the fear that the fire might slacken under way, and the increased draught due to the motion of the train caused it to 'liven up', not even setting the handle to full 'Off' could dissipate the impression among the passengers inside the carriage that they were in the lead-roofed *piombi* of Venice, on the hottest of summer's days.

Steam heating, using the steam from the engine, is the customary method for winter working of steam-hauled trains in Great Britain and many other countries. For such heating, all carriages in the train must be equipped with continuous steam-piping, and connecting hoses at the ends. When this is impossible, special small heating boilers in special 'heating tenders' are required.

Even then, there are many tricky points arising in connexion with steam heating. Today, even on the latest European international expresses, the first carriages near the engine can become overheated, since the steam passes in directly from the boiler, while at the tail of the train it is difficult to keep up a comfortable temperature, the steam having lost a great deal of its heating power in passing through the long pipes and many radiators on the way. The water formed by condensation of the steam must be drawn off, and the regulating handles, which can be controlled by the passengers in the different compartments, must function properly. Some trains, therefore, use hot water instead of steam, as this is considerably more moderate in its action and can be controlled with less inconvenience. Also it retains its heat more effectively in the long pipe-lines. On electric railways electric heating is, of course, the natural means, and this method has great and significant advantages over other systems.

It has probably never occurred to the majority of us that ventilation can prove to be a source of grave difficulties on a moving train. We might pardonably have assumed that it would be sufficient simply to open a window, and let the clear, fresh air blow all the cobwebs away. Unfortunately, coal-smoke and the wet steam clouds from the engine can find their way in at the same time. An open window in a tunnel, moreover, can bring discomfort to a whole carriage full of passengers. Ventilators are therefore used which admit the fresh, outside air and draw off the foul air from each compartment without allowing too much smoke or dust to enter. Diesel or electric trains solve this problem quite simply. There *is* no smoke or steam.

The passengers on many railways are compulsory members of a 'class society' with rigid boundaries. The colour of the ticket puts the passenger in his place with no false sentiment. For many years third class was the mainstay of railway operation and economy, but in 1956 it was abolished in Europe, and the old third was renamed second; the second class became first; then there are the aristocratic Pullman and other trains commanding supplementary fares. The Germans, with a nice sense of social gradations, once had a *fourth* class—the lowest category to which a passenger could descend, but this has been abolished.

Modern developments have increased the passengers' comfort in all classes, more particularly in the democratic second. On many railways, the modern second-class is even more comfortable than some first-class carriages of bygone days. All standards of railway passenger comfort are, however, ultimately governed by the general standard of life and comfort obtaining in the particular country. In the United States, officially democratic, there are many graduations in its train accommodation, ranging from 'coaches' with adjustable seats to Pullman drawing-room cars and Pullman sleeping cars of many types up to those with 'master room' suites which even include shower-baths. The supplement charged varies with the luxury of the accommodation.

The Scandinavian countries, Norway in particular, approach 'railway democracy' from another angle. First-class dining and sleeping services, *etc.*, are generally available to passengers with second-class tickets. *All* trains carry second-class accommodation, but first-class may be omitted. The pampered passenger will seek in vain for '*Blue Trains*', '*Golden Arrows*' and all the American '*Limited*' types.

The possibility of making up a train of different classes and types of rolling stock, in different proportions, itself represents an advantage

The 'Train of Tomorrow'. The so-called day car with easy chairs which look very comfortable. They should offer the apotheothis of luxury, since they were designed on the basis of innumerable measurements and after lengthy experiments by a leading anatomical expert of Harvard University. In the background is the way up to the astrodome.

The 'Train of Tomorrow'. The dining car also has its 'top storey', where, under the transparent vault of the astrodome, the view and the food—both excellently served—can be enjoyed together.

typical of railway operation, but modern trends are diverging from this goal of flexibility towards the ideal of the 'standard set'—the train permanently made up of the same arrangement and number of vehicles. Among such are to be included the more or less famous and well-known expresses. Scandinavia has developed the 'lightning' train (*lyntog*)—electric or diesel—with motor cars back and front and a trailer in between. The train works 'push-and-pull', equally well in either direction. Although the trains are called 'lightning', the speeds they attain do not exceed 75 m.p.h. The steep gradients and sharp curves offer little encouragement to would-be record-breakers.

But, top speeds apart, another factor in successful train operation is consistency and punctuality. Here records vary all over Europe. France holds pride of place with well over 90 per cent. of its trains arriving at their destinations on time; in Norway 90 per cent. of all passenger trains are never more than 5 minutes late. Italy, which can boast of numerous high speed trains, has but a poor record in this respect: 43 per cent. of all trains are more than 5 minutes late, 39 per cent more than 15 minutes late.

A railway, with all its permanent way and buildings, locomotives and rolling stock, its staff of employees in and outside the trains, on the line, in offices, in engineering and administrative departments, is a giant machine—a 'service' of imposing size whether State-owned, nationalized or run by private enterprise. The machine may appear to be a little slow and conservative. This is perhaps inevitable when operating on such a vast scale. Any innovation may have unforeseen consequences elsewhere. Changes must be introduced without upsetting the balance of the whole, complicated, smoothly-running machinery. No wonder the men at the top tend to be cautious in their decisions, and think twice before jumping after something new! We are all the safer for that.

In heavy goods, and even in light goods traffic, the railways still retain a position which is as yet unassailed and almost unassailable. The battle centering round the passenger traffic continues, however, over the heads of the passengers. The air-lines seek to make them air-minded, while road and rail interests fight for those who remain earth-bound. According to statistics, which can prove anything—and sometimes even the right thing—American railways lost 426 million dollars on their passenger traffic in 1947. That is a figure to give food for thought. In the United States, the most highly mechanized country in the world, aeroplane and motor-coach are attracting the travelling public so widely that the railways can hold their passengers only by offering them a standard of comfort and luxury which is uneconomically high. This, at least, is suggested by the figures.

This is not very encouraging, though one important factor must not be forgotten. The characteristic feature of a railway system, which

The 'Train of Tomorrow'—a close-up of the astrodome car. The complete 'train set' consists of day 'coaches,' restaurant car, Pullman observation car, and Pullman Sleeping cars.

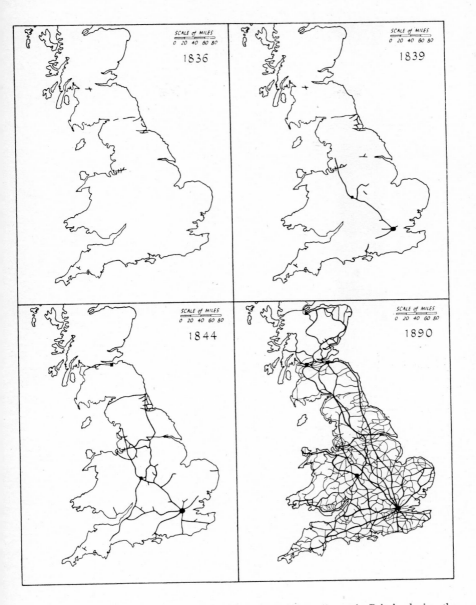

These four maps show the remarkable development of the railways in Britain during the first sixty years of railway history. In 1836 the pioneer lines between Stockton and Darlington, and Liverpool and Machester, had been extended and added to in the neighbouring coal-mining districts. There were also short isolated railways near Glasgow and in Cornwall. The first line from London was in existence by 1839, and by 1844 there were four complete lines linking the east and west coasts.

An artist's impression of new trains planned for the Chesapeake & Ohio Railroad. This shows that a remarkable change may take place in the general appearance of the train of tomorrow. Instead of an assembly of coupled, separate vehicles, with a locomotive at the head, the coming shape of the railway may develop into a long, articulated line, of which the motive power unit (the 'locomotive' of old) forms a 'head', like that of the conventional dragon.

impresses itself on the whole economy of railway operation, is the immense capital invested. Or, more aptly, the invested capital is there, and a great part of the annual running cost is determined by it, whether the railway carries much or little traffic. Hence, the railway may lose a little on a single passenger, but profit ultimately from carrying 10,000,000 of them. This is quite a normal phenomenon—that the turnover makes the profit—but there are few branches of trade and industry in which this is so marked as in the case of railways.

It must be stressed that the railway is primarily a means of *transport*, and not only a form of *travel*. The railway puts us in a container on wheels, and transports us from place to place along a track which has been planned and laid *in order to carry things*. The fact that while in transit we pass through beautiful and interesting scenery, dive into holes underground, cross great rivers, see new scenes and form new impressions, is, from the railwayman's point of view, a secondary consideration and an unimportant accompaniment. Let the train be late—you have enjoyed its comfort and the wonderful scenery all the longer and for the same fare! The passenger ought to be ashamed of complaining! He is being carried swiftly from place to place, with all the amenities and all the scenery included in the price of the ticket. But unfortunately passengers do not always appreciate this point of view.

There are, of course, people who *must* travel from place to place, and who are compelled to get somewhere in the shortest possible time. Such people now have a widening choice between trains, buses and aircraft. It is therefore necessary to woo them, in some measure, or else the railways will find themselves, like old spinsters, left sitting while the skyways and the highways seduce their passengers from them.

In Europe, even before the last war, there were numbers of first-rate and most luxurious trains, like the *Orient Express* and the *Blue Train* (London-Dover-Calais-Paris-Nice-San Remo). In these, the international 'Wagon-Lits' company ran their sleeping-cars, in which, for the equivalent of several pounds, the international traveller could reserve a small complete compartment, with a 'lit' that was really a bed. These trains, however wonderful and full of improvements, were designed on purely traditional lines. The vehicles composing them were simply developments of the original, primitive forms.

The first really radical changes in railway train design and construction have appeared in the United States. Pictures show more clearly than words can tell the forthcoming revolution in railway passenger comfort. A new look, a new line has appeared in the designs and projects. The *California Zephyr*, standing in Chicago's Union Station, is a revelation in new forms, a shining monster of stainless steel. Life should be good in this hotel on wheels, with its lounges, smoke-rooms, bedrooms, bathrooms, its restaurant and bar, all air-conditioned and controlled for temperature and humidity. As the *Zephyr* rushes towards the sunny Californian landscape at 90 m.p.h., the passenger on the 'upper deck' under the astrodome can view the passing scene in all comfort. That is the true sense and pleasure of *travel*. On alighting at San Francisco, he has not only been transported over more than 2,500 miles, but has also spent two days in pleasant and stimulating travel and comfortable sight-seeing.

It is obvious that in recent years American railway travel has been inoculated with some very novel ideas. A new and powerful impulse has been given by General Motors, an interesting fact, since the name is more familiar in the motor-car world. Surprisingly, the world's greatest car-builders appear to have turned to the railway for fresh conquests. It is interesting to find 'car people' coming to the help of the 'railway people' in their competitive struggle with the motor car!

The General Motors development throws an interesting new light on the whole road-*v*.-rail controversy. Originally, the contest was between the petrol engine on the highway and the steam engine on the railway. The victorious invasion of the railway by the diesel locomotive in the United States has, however, brought the motor manufacturer on the side of the railway. Diesels follow each other closely on the roads and the railways, and General Motors supply the engines for both. The old competitor, the internal combustion engine, has at last conquered the railway and given it new life for its struggle with the roads. At the present time, practically all the American big-name trains are diesel-hauled, and General Motors are creating the train of tomorrow.

It is said that some of the firm's engineers made journeys from Chicago to the Pacific in the cabs of some diesel locomotives. They were impressed by the clear view from the cab windows and conceived the idea of providing something similar for the benefit of the passengers. The outcome was the design of a completely new train on unconventional lines. The suggestion was pursued further in collaboration with railway authorities and carriage builders such as Pullman. All these experts—not merely established engineers but men who had acquired their training and their knowledge in the whole field of land transport —put their heads together to create a new type of railway train, which was run all over the North American Continent as a travelling exhibition, a herald of new ideas.

CHAPTER VII

TRAIN OF THE FUTURE

THE simplest form of railway vehicle is a box on four wheels. It may even appear to be the only basic form possible. Why four wheels? Well, there is a pair of rails, and three wheels—the minimum for stability—would be rather out of balance. Starting from this consideration, improvements follow. Railway vehicles, and passenger carriages in particular, become longer but more difficult to handle on curves. Then appears the bogie, or 'truck', one at each end and each at first with four wheels, making eight wheels in all per vehicle. There follows the invention of the six-wheel bogie, producing the 'twelve-wheeler' passenger coach. This has been, and still is, the general line of development of railway rolling stock in most countries.

But one day a man comes into the railway offices—a man from outside. He is no railwayman, has no railway experience, no prejudices. He has 'an idea'—a very good idea, in his view. It is concerned with wheels. No—not what you probably think, not merely an advance to sixteen wheels or any greater number of wheels. Far the reverse. He wants to go back to the obvious simplicity of the minimum—*two* wheels. No more and no less.

Consternation in the railway camp! Quite an ingenious idea. So ingenious, in fact, that the very locomotives seem to greet it with an amused grin! Certainly it would ease the railway budget unconscionably to be able to dispense with large numbers of superfluous wheels. On second thoughts, that would also produce a saving in weight, precious tons, on the already groaningly overweighted passenger trains. The suggestion now begins to appear more interesting. No real engineer is afraid of looking a startling suggestion squarely in the face. The question of 'how' can be left for subsequent consideration. As a matter of fact, in spite of bogies, pony-trucks, swinging axles and the like, a railway train is not as flexible as a snake on curves. The 'lead', the amount of deflection between the locomotive and each succeeding carriage or truck as it takes the bend in turn, is far from sufficient. The carriage body is over the wheels, all the heavy weights are high up, and the tendency to swing and tip over is increased. Hence, speed must be reduced on curves, and the 'running-speed' becomes much less than the top speed of which the engine is capable.

Something should be done, obviously, to mitigate these inconveniences. Only some really novel engineering development could be of service here. It is, however, one thing to realize that something must be done, and even to acknowledge *what* must be done, but quite another to see how to do it, as many a hapless engineer has found to his cost.

As is so often the case with technical progress, the impulse this time came from an 'unestablished' outsider, a man less under the spell of tradition and practice. A lieutenant-colonel in the Spanish Army Engineers, one Alejandro Goicoechea Omar, appeared on the scene in 1941 with a project for an 'articulated train set', consisting of units each some twenty feet long. The actual novel feature is the provision of only two wheels per unit. These are placed at the very rear or tail

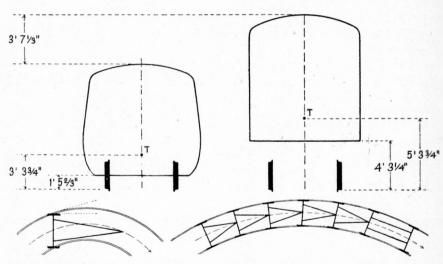

The diagram above shows clearly how in the Talgo system (on the left) the carriage is pressed down against the rails, compared with the existing arrangement (on the right). The centre of gravity T has been lowered a full two feet. The sketch at the bottom shows the perfect articulation in curves, thanks to the characteristic Talgo feature of three-point suspension. There is otherwise a danger, when running through curves, that the outside wheel on the curve will lift or 'climb' on the outer rail with its whole flange. The slightly exaggerated sketch, bottom left, shows that the Talgo system wheel 'turns in' with reference to the rail, and thus acts to prevent derailment.

'TALGO' is an experimental train, built of aluminium, with 75 per cent less weight, and on an entirely new and revolutionary principle. The fundamental idea is startlingly original— only two (2) wheels under each carriage! When each carriage is hooked on to a pivot on the one in front, the whole train becomes as lissom as a snake, bending smoothly in the curves and with such a low centre of gravity that it can take even sharp bends at high speed. 'Dead weight' has always been the railway engineer's bugbear, both technically and financially. If the 'Talgo' system can really produce a light, steady and flexibly-linked train, this Spanish invention, allied to American engineering skill, could initiate a true revolution in railway passenger transport.

end of the unit. Obviously, such a vehicle, on two back wheels only, could not travel far alone. It would nose over and dig itself into the permanent way. The lieutenant-colonel has made provision for this. The front end of each unit carriage is pivoted, or hung, on to the rear of the unit in front. This is the simple device, the Columbus egg, which has fundamentally changed the outlook in passenger-train engineering, and brought with it a number of startlingly ingenious solutions of associated problems.

The sketch-drawing of the arrangement reproduced at the foot of p. 226 will give even the technical layman a good understanding of the manner in which each carriage is made to follow the carriage immediately in front. The whole train is reminiscent of those toy, jointed snakes on wheels, which some readers may remember having in their childhood. The more detailed drawing on the left shows a little more of the technicalities of the arrangement. It is easy to see that the outside wheel no longer tends to lift off the rail in a curve, and upset the train. On the contrary, friction on the rising wheel flange will press the wheel down *on* the rail and prevent derailment.

These features already represent engineering advantages, but in addition, the wheels are no longer linked by continuous axles, and furthermore, are arranged so far back as to come between two carriage units. Thus, the carriage floor, instead of being supported *over* the wheels, hangs *between* them and can be dropped lower. This dispenses with the need to climb steps in order to enter the carriage, or with the provision of specially high platforms, as in England; and, more important still, the centre of gravity of the carriage can be lowered a good two feet. That is, indeed, a gift from the gods. The centre of gravity is the point where the centrifugal force is concentrated, which tends to tilt and upset the carriage on the curves; and this centrifugal force now acts lower down and with less effect providing considerably more safety for the passengers.

Since the almost perfect articulation gives steadiness in curves, the train does not require weight to confer stability and smooth running. All advantages of modern, light construction, can therefore be utilized. The saving in weight is imposing, and in addition to ensuring steady running on curves it allows 25 per cent higher running speed between stations. Even modern engineering progress can show few other such startling advances.

Three such trains have already been built. One, on the Spanish 5 ft. 3 in. gauge, runs between Madrid and the French frontier; the other two are standard-gauge trains in America, operated by the Lackawanna Railroad system in New Jersey. All three are diesel-electric, and the locomotives weigh only 135 lb. per horse-power—about the lowest weight on record.

The name of the train itself—TALGO—is not the least interesting of its features. While quite short and incisive, it embodies a whole history in its make-up. T for 'train', A for 'articulated', L for 'light', G for Goicoechea, the inventor, and O for Oriol, the Spanish industrialist who financed the invention. The Americans add 'ACF', for American Car and Foundry Company, the builders.

The railway has a long and glorious history. Undoubtedly, it has been the great weapon in the conquest of the world, by and for mankind; it is one of the most powerful linking-factors of world civilization. Although now it may appear to be suffering displacement by automobilism and aviation, it has nevertheless ruled the roost through one of the most revolutionary epochs of history, and has engraved its name for all time on human memory. The railway has gathered laurels aplenty, and has the right to a funeral with full pomp and ceremony!

Yet we may be a little premature in thinking in terms of obsequies. Is the railway in fact on the point of death?

It is true that while until quite recently the railway appeared as a positive incarnation of scientific and engineering progress, in the twentieth century the motor-car and the aeroplane have tended increasingly to steal the picture. These smart and speedy creations

A somewhat unusual railway picture. This shows how easy it is to step out of a Talgo train carriage. Not that the platform is specially high! The carriage floor has been lowered to within inches of the top of the rails. The lady will surely excuse us if we choose to call to mind the days when we boosted Grannie or Auntie up or down the steep steps of the old-time railway 'coaches' when on a Continental holiday!

seem to bring an even more powerful promise of progress and adventure, potentialities and prospects. The railway has been thrust into the background. It already appears a little old, stiff and ossified. That at least was the picture until only a few years ago; at the present moment it is no longer so. As the earlier pages have shown, the voice of the railway has been heard again, and not merely as a death-rattle or an obituary notice. On the contrary, there are signs of reviving life in an organism which appeared to have sunk into a faint lethargy, almost a trance, but now again begins to stir in a manner showing both vitality and large reserves of power.

New competitors need not always bring death to the old in their wake. Competition itself may prove the stimulus to renewed effort. There are many examples of this to be found in the history of engineering. With the advent of broadcasting, there were many who prophesied

Anything peculiar about this picture? Yes. Usually the travellers hang half way out of the windows, bending down to bid farewell to their friends on the platform. Here it is the other way round, showing how low the floor of a Talgo train carriage can be dropped, thanks to its revolutionary 'two-wheels' arrangement. This change has been made not merely to make farewells more comfortable, but also to enable smoother (and faster!) running on curves

the death of the gramophone. Actually, the apparently hopeless rivalry ended with the revival of the gramophone in the form of the radiogram. There is every chance, therefore, that the competitive challenge forced on the railway by road and air services, which has been willingly taken up, may be the start of a new chapter in railway history.

There is, of course, always a certain conservative spirit in railway matters, due, naturally, to some of the essential features of railway operation. Trains run on earthbound railway tracks are necessarily tied to rigid, timetable schedules. One wheel—not under the train, but in the 'system'—must operate another wheel, constantly and with exactitude. The least alteration entails such consequences that there is a natural inclination to avoid changes. This conservative attitude, however, proves also, as we have already seen, to be something of a virtue. The reliability of the whole vast organization requires certain safeguards against untimely interference and unnecessary experimentation. Nothing must be done or decided without previous thorough examination of all possible direct or indirect consequences. This principle, in itself most reasonable, is to some extent dangerous in that it implies a tendency to rigidity, to stagnation. Intense competition from outside may, however, provide the needed stimulant—the 'corpse-reviver'—necessary for creative railway development. A tireless activity is developing on all sides in the railway world, a testing and experimenting with new possibilities, new plans, new features, with an energy which can only be fully appreciated when we realize the complex and manifold nature of the problems awaiting solution.

The direction which will be taken in future railway development is not yet clearly indicated. It is certain only that there will be no decline. For instance, it is difficult to see how the other means of transport, the highways and airways, could undertake to handle the millions of ton-miles of transport services now handled annually by the railway systems. There is, in fact, little prospect of these competitors being able to take over the burden, either now or at any later date. The railway is indispensable, and must keep on running, though it is not easy to predict in what directions the railways will develop in order to satisfy today's needs.

There is, in the first place, the question of speed, and this means speed of transportation, not miles per hour. Impressed by the fantastic records on the road and in the air, many are inclined to be pessimistic about the railway's power to hold its own in this mad race. Certainly, as we sit in the 'up local', reading of John Cobb's 394 m.p.h. in the Utah salt desert, or the English *Comet* civil aircraft, which covers the mile in a flat 7 seconds, it would appear that travelling by train is something of an insult to our present age of speed. This impression is, however, unjustified.

Cobb may well have covered a mile in just over 9 seconds, but he never ran a whole hour at that speed, nor indeed could he. A modern express train, on the other hand, can run at 90 m.p.h., hour after hour, unless stopped by adverse signals, and this performance could even be bettered by trains of the *Talgo* type. This is a feat unequalled for a comparable length of time, even by a car on a good road. Thus, although the railway may be somewhat short of wind where the aeroplane is concerned, it can still compete effectively with the lorries and the buses on the roads in regard to speeds maintained on long runs in ordinary service. This is the consideration which affects the bulk of the traffic. There is no reason to doubt that the railway will continue in the future also to remain competitive on this basis. A locomotive, hauling numbers of carriages containing hundreds of passengers, is

o

not easily beaten by a car or a bus, carrying its half-dozen or few dozen passengers, between towns some hundreds of miles apart.

In competition with the airways, where the railway is admittedly far inferior in the matter of speed, other factors intervene to restore the balance, as regards the service afforded to passengers and goods. It is very convenient to travel fast, but the decisive factor for the passenger is the total time spent going from place to place—or more precisely, from house to house. And there is also the question of *what* time. Can the passenger 'sleep through' from point to point? We have already seen how the sleeping-car can bring the passenger along in practically 'no' time. This is a measure of the value of a means of travel to the general passenger.

Two places are one 'train night' apart. The business man has his customary night's rest, drops off the train after breakfast, and reaches his office, or his customers, at the usual time. A fast passenger aircraft may take, say, two hours actual flying, between the same two places. With a bare hour travelling time to and from the airports at each end, that is three hours in all. If the same business man wishes to be in the office at nine in the morning, he must, therefore, queue for his airport

A pair of Talgo trains are now in regular service in Spain, the inventor's own country, running on the 500 mile stretch between Madrid and the French frontier. These graceful, glittering aluminium trains are forerunners of a new and revolutionary future, in sharp contrast to the ageless romance of the countryside through which they daily pass on their swift journeyings.

bus at the departure end at about five in the morning. Quite early enough for most people, too early for many! The alarm-clock trills its cheery (!) message at 4 a.m. Nearly four hours' sleep lost. His more conservative opposite number in the night train has lost no sleep. He needs 'no' time for travel. Whoever thinks this is a sophistry, and therefore no practical argument, may find himself one day, sleepy and hungry after his flying adventures, beaten by his well-fed and wide-awake competitor 'just off the night train'.

Whoever may think such considerations nonsensical may well appreciate the second factor in the problem—the question of cost. In daily practical life it is not only hours that count, but pennies. Time and money can be accurately measured against each other. This very real fact is a help to the airlines in their competition with other means of transport. Flying is undoubtedly the dearest form of travel in ordinary circumstances. This is obvious from the cost of fuel, material and labour, for which the traveller must pay; but if time is included in the calculation a different result is obtained. An airline ticket is dearer than a railway ticket for the same distance; but the air route 'costs' less time and the ultimate decision may, therefore, be against the railway.

However, yet another factor intervenes in the argument. The same rate of exchange between time and money does not always apply in all cases. Take an imaginary example: a day's travel by train costs five pounds; the same distance by air, seven pounds ten shillings. The train journey, however, if undertaken in the daytime, implies the loss of one working day. Therefore, the cost of one working day must be added to the railway fare. Calculating soberly, it is probable that the loss of wages, earnings, profits—in one word, income—for one working day may amount to more than the odd fifty shillings difference between rail and air travel. It is actually cheaper to fly. Many travellers find themselves in this position; they fly everywhere, and save money in the process.

The great mass of travellers, however, do not need to value their time in pounds sterling per hour. People travel quite regularly third-class instead of first in order to save money. Most people, therefore, will find it cheaper to travel by rail than by air. This is an important, perhaps a decisive advantage in the contest between the railways and the airways.

How far the railways can improve running speeds by lightweight trains, railcars or rail buses is as yet uncertain. They will certainly not push development beyond the limits of prudence in regard to punctuality, reliability and safety. These are such important assets in the competition of railways with other forms of transport that they must be retained at all costs. The firm, smooth track and the separate, exclusive right-of-way are the factors which enable railway transportation to function as a high-precision mechanism. Even taking this into account, however, railway speeds are still capable of considerable improvement without sacrificing any vital advantages.

With regard to the problem of high speed, the railway has, however, some peculiar difficulties of its own to overcome. It has already been explained how the railway's motive power, the locomotive, occupies a special position among self-propelled vehicles in that it requires a certain minimum 'adhesion weight' to perform its task properly. In all other cases, the striving is towards less and less 'weight per horse-power'. For aircraft, this is the decisive factor of the whole design, and it is only the modern internal-combustion engine, with its favourable weight-to-power ratio, which has made mechanical flight possible. For ships, the weight of the propelling machinery is also a most important economic factor, for the maximum possible capacity for cargo must be ensured. For the railway locomotive, as we have already seen, the problem assumes quite a different aspect. The tractive force cannot exceed the frictional force between wheels and rails. The frictional force is determined in the first instance by the weight, or pressure, on the

The night train, covering 5–600 miles in a night, may be said to give its sleeping-car passengers a journey in 'no' time: sleep is in any case necessary, so no *additional* time has been spent in travelling. Similarly, without using more powerful locomotives or higher speeds, it is possible, as proved today on the German expresses, to *save* the travelling businessman time on journeys, by providing office and secretarial facilities; what is really travelling time, becomes 'useful' working time. Thus the time spent ('wasted') in rushing around by car is not lost on the railway.

The Talgo train. Here, two carriages are shown coupled together; the gap is enclosed by a flexible bellows which, when drawn aside, shows the powerful springs on the wheel, and reveals the fact that the wheel hub is not under the carriage itself, but in the gap between.

rails (the 'adhesion weight') and a frictional coefficient, depending on the material, which (for steel on steel) has a value of about 0·25.

A heavy locomotive, however, is not particularly suitable when speed has to be increased, and there are, essentially, two ways in which the necessary adhesion weight of a locomotive can be reduced. The first is to reduce the weight of the load hauled; i.e., use lighter rolling-stock. Railway history shows no indications of any trend in this direction. On the contrary, the demand for increased safety and comfort has steadily pushed the weights of railway carriages higher and higher. It is only of late years that the competition of road and air services has forced the railways to experiment more or less boldly with lighter carriages, such as, for instance, those of the *Talgo* train. Even should the results of this relatively short-lived experiment seem promising, it is too early to make any conclusive forecasts. A true reversion from heavy to lighter rolling-stock can only be expected after the results of present experiments with light vehicles have given reliable proof of their safety and satisfactory durability under conditions of hard, daily and continuous service.

On the other hand, in theory at least, lighter rolling-stock in the trains is not the only means of reducing the engine-weight required. Under otherwise identical conditions, the adhesion weight can be reduced if the locomotive wheels can grip the rails better. For example, it might be possible to increase the friction between wheels and rails by making them of other materials. The analogy of motor tyres has been frequently made, and the suggestion as frequently rejected. The objections to the use of pneumatic rubber tyres on railway engines are so obvious and so serious that most suggestions to this effect will simply have been pigeon-holed. The perspectives revealed by the mere possibility of using pneumatic tyres on trains are, however, so attractive that certain ideas have been found worthy of serious development. It was not merely the possibility of increasing friction that gave life to the idea of using rubber tyres. A further prospect is opened up—the possibility of solving one of the most awkward problems of railway engineering.

The rail track, or permanent way, has one very weak point—the necessary gap at the rail joints. Rails are rolled in suitable shapes or profiles, and in lengths from about 39 to 100 feet. Until recent years it has always been supposed that any one rail cannot be welded to the preceding rail, as in the case of street tramway track, so that the wheels can run over the junction without shocks or jolts. This although very costly, would be an excellent method. But the rails expand with heat, and contract with cold. If they are not fixed firmly in the ground, as are tramway rails in the street paving, expansion would inevitably cause buckling or sideways deflection of the track if the rails were welded together or joined butt to butt. But experience now proves that given firm holding down of the rails throughout their length, the

The only two wheels the Talgo train carriage possesses are set right back and overlap into the gap between two carriages. They are individually suspended without through axles, so that the carriage floor can be dropped nearly to rail level.

The remarkably smooth running of the old G.W.R.'s broad gauge trains was partly due to the fact that the sleepers ran lengthwise beneath the rails, instead of across them. Each length of rail was thus supported to its very end, but cross-ties were necessary to keep the sleepers the right distance apart. Note the quaint signals.

tendency to expand or contract can be confined within them as a temporarily unrelieved stress. As a result rail welding has now taken place on a considerable scale, and sometimes over lengthy stretches of track.

All breaks in continuity of the railway track are, of course, highly undesirable. As a wheel approaches the rail joint, the end of the rail is bent down a little below the level of the next rail on to which the wheel must pass. The wheel thus has to 'climb up' on to the next rail, and it is bound to strike against the end of it. This process is repeated for every wheel in the train at every joint on the track, and involves—particularly in the case of heavy express trains—an enormous amount of wear and tear, both on the rails and on the wheels. The shocks and jolts at the rail joints are also most uncomfortable for those travelling on the train. A fortune has awaited the man who could invent a perfect rail joint, which would be free from these disabilities. Many have tried to win the prize without success, but rail welding has now solved the problem. Another attempt at a solution was by fitting the wheels with pneumatic rubber tyres, for it was found that rubber tyres made light of the small cracks between the rails.

It was not enough, however, merely to fix rubber tyres on the existing wheels. The introduction of pneumatic tyres would cause a complete reversal in the trend of railway motive power engineering. To replace ponderous locomotives and heavy coaches, light motor-driven units and passenger trailers have to be designed. This involves an appreciable reduction in the tractive force required, a reduction to only a fraction of the power required to steam-haul a modern heavy express train, in which the carriages are by preference made heavy to ensure steady running as free as possible from shocks and jolts. Since the friction between rubber and steel is three times that between steel and steel, only one-third of the former adhesion weight is required to obtain the same tractive force; and since the latter is itself much reduced by the adoption of lighter construction, very light and economical motive-power units can be employed. The rubber tyres do not wear down appreciably on the smooth steel rails and, more especially, do not bump on the rail joints. Thus the life of the rails is increased, while trains run far more smoothly and comfortably than has even been previously possible with steel on steel.

A 'railbus' built by the French firm of Michelin, and introduced for branch services on the French railways. The driver's cab has become a sort of 'conning tower', with a clear view in both directions of travel.

A view of the driver's 'conning tower' in one of the novel 'railbuses' built by Michelin for the French Railways. It is impossible to see much difference between operating this and driving a car. The railbus itself is motor-driven, and the driver uses a clutch, exactly as in a road vehicle. On the other hand, there is (of course) no steering wheel.

The 'Dovre Express' Norway's fastest train, passing the summit at Hjerkinn, between Oslo and Trondhjem (Drosstheim), 3,360 feet above sea level. The train is timed at 45 m.p.h., end to end. Not a bad effort for a line climbing from sea level to the height of Ben Lomond, with curves down to 820 feet (12 chains) radius.

The first rubber-tyred rail vehicle was a rebuilt 40 h.p. Renault motor car. The wheels had narrow-tread tyres, somewhat similar to those used on motor buses prior to the invention of balloon tyres. The steering gear and mudguards were, of course, removed. Round, dished plates were fixed on the inside of the wheels, projecting well beyond the tyres and acting thus as flanges to hold the wheels on the track. This experimental vehicle was made and tested by the Michelin Company in all secrecy until the results were ripe for the Press. On the 26th January, 1931, the first official trial run was made with a similar vehicle, a 20 h.p. Panhard.

The experiments were continued until immediately before the last war, and finally arrived at the 'omnibus train' of separately-driven cars, each carrying 24 passengers. Speeds reached from 75 to 78 m.p.h., and the petrol consumption was just over 11·3 miles per gallon. The cars had 6 wheels in front, and 4 in the rear. A great saving was obtained in dead weight (tare). While an ordinary passenger train weighs about 1 ton tare for each passenger carried, this figure was reduced in the case of the 'rail-bus' to not quite 4 cwt. per passenger.

The implications of this saving can be illustrated by the following Norwegian example. A train running between Oslo and Trondheim has to climb 3,360 feet to summit level at Hjerkinn. Each passenger, and also the proportionate weight of his 'tare'—locomotive, carriages, etc.—has to be lifted 3,360 feet high before being again lowered to his destination. If the total weight per passenger at 1·6 ton, the total work to be done is 5,376 foot-tons per passenger. For a rail-bus on rubber wheels this figure is reduced to 1,008 foot-tons, which is quite a considerable saving. A daily run each, with 24 passengers, would save in a year enough energy to lift 350,000 tons to a height of 80 feet.

The Michelin Company have rendered pioneer service with a view to enabling us to travel 'softly' by rail. A start was made with this train running between Strasbourg and Paris. Pneumatic tyres require the load to be well distributed. The railway carriage is developing, if not into an actual centipede, at least into a 'twenty-wheeler'.

Unfortunately, it appears that we shall have to wait a long time before pneumatic tyres replace steel on all railway wheels. It remains an attractively promising suggestion. The present system of steel on steel, hard metal tyres continually bumping over metal rail-joints, is too rough a process for good engineering practice. If 90-foot rails are used, an express train will run over about 5,000 rail lengths in an hour. On the basis of 12 standard carriages and a 'Pacific' type locomotive (4–6–2 wheels), there will be 150 forcible blows at the rail joints *per second*! This is a strong plea in favour of the ideal solution, with rubber-tyred wheels rolling over the perfect 'road-surface'—which is, in fact, what a railway track represents.

The principal difficulty is to make the pneumatic tyres sufficiently strong. It is a 'wearing' life for rubber, supporting a railway carriage; far more so than supporting a motor-car. There are two reasons for this. First, a railway carriage weighs far more than any vehicle on the roads, and second, the narrow rail necessitates a far smaller tread on the tyre. On the road, the tyre itself can flatten and broaden, to carry a heavier weight. As in balloon and 'camel-pad' tyres, the area in contact with the road can be increased to keep the unit pressure on the tyre sufficiently low. It is this pressure which determines the load on the

On the right, the body of a carriage for the 'quiet train' between Paris and Strasbourg is being lowered on to its ten-wheel bogies. The pneumatic tyre on the steel rail represents a union of the ideal wheel and the ideal road surface. The buffers too (top, left) are of rubber.

tyre. Thus, large motor-lorries carrying heavy loads have wide tyre-treads, and, in many cases, double or even multiple tyres—more wheels side by side. The road itself offers space enough to carry them.

On the railway, conditions are different. The top surfaces of the pair of rails constitute the 'road' surface. This is only a couple of inches wide. (The maximum for the heaviest rail sections used in Britain is $3'' + 3'' = 6''$). No broader bearing surface can be obtained however wide the tyres are made. Nor would any designer contemplate running a broad tread tyre on a narrow rail. There must be a narrow tread

The 'railcar' bids fair to fill the gap between rail travel and bus travel. This shows a self-propelled railway passenger carriage, of stainless steel, holding 90 passengers and equipped with two Diesel engines with hydraulic transmission, totalling 550 horsepower, which can achieve a speed of 60 miles an hour within two minutes from the start, and attain a maximum of 85 m.p.h. The carriage is air-conditioned and tastefully fitted. Such railcars are being built by the Budd works in Philadelphia, and as 'lightweight trains' are coming into use on many American railways.

running on an equally narrow rail; that is an inescapable condition. As a result, the unit pressure on the rubber tread is very high, and presents a most difficult problem for the tyre-maker.

Michelin undertook a bold step indeed in tackling this knotty problem in the 1920's—a step which required long, scientific and technical research, and a multitude of experiments, tests and trials, before satisfactory results could be obtained. It implied, further, a large-scale approach to manufacturing and production problems, and the consideration of numberless subsidiary details, before a solution could be found. A considerable amount of time, labour and money had to be thrown into the balance for a problematic, ultimate advantage. Fortunately, France had, in the brothers André and Edouard Michelin, two men of modern outlook, with the courage needed to undertake the task and the pertinacity to carry it to a successful conclusion. They did not allow themselves to be discouraged even by their own engineers and technicians, who started by announcing categorically that to try to run a pneumatic tyre on a railway line was like trying to run bare-foot on a knife-blade!

It would, in fact, have been impossible to solve this difficult technical problem while retaining the old, heavy type of railway carriage and the ordinary arrangement of four-wheel bogies, *i.e.*, eight wheels per carriage. First, the weight of the carraigehad to be drastically reduced, and next, this reduced weight had to be distributed over more wheels. It was not possible to use the method adopted in the case of motor lorries, and put more wheels side by side. In consequence, the additional wheels had to be arranged as closely together as possible, *along* the rails. This led to designs for ten-wheel bogies; thus producing 'twenty-wheeler' carriages.

The trim, new carriages of this type that were constructed in France had their weight brought down to between 14 and 15 tons (13·9 tons for the passenger-carriage proper, 14·7 tons for the refreshment car). With the designed full load of 64 passengers the total weight was still under 20 tons, which, distributed over the 20 wheels, was a load of not quite one ton on each tyre. This was, in fact, the target weight for the tyre designer. Pneumatic tyres able to carry one ton, even on a 'knife-edge' (as represented by the rail), are within the power of the modern tyre manufacturers.

These are no longer self-propelled rail motor-vehicles, *i.e.*, 'rail buses', but normal passenger trains which went into regular service between Paris and Strasbourg. These trains deserved a more than momentary attention: they were the first *quiet* railway trains in the world.

But there seems little likelihood of such silent trains coming into general service. The tyre maintenance proved to be a matter of constant

Train ferries are a familiar and typical example of a link in the transport chain, by which goods are brought to their destination without transhipment on the way. The train ferry just putting out from Milwaukee harbour is about to close its capacious maw, which has just swallowed 32 fully-laden goods trucks.

expense, and the lightness of the vehicles was such that whatever advantage they derived from silent running tended to be nullified by rough riding. As a result, no further rolling-stock of this description has been built by the progressive French railways. Two similar coaches built by the Swiss Federal Railways were the subject of patient experiment, but were soon withdrawn from main line trains and finished their service on a quiet branch. The long-distance French rubber-tyred train has also been withdrawn from the main line over which it ran. Work on the development of lighter train-units, principally in the form of self-propelled rail-cars, has been pushed forward industriously on all the world's railways in recent years. This will certainly affect short-distance traffic. The system has advantages in operating economy: rail cars are cheap to run, and the greater train frequency possible will serve to attract more passengers to the railways. The result will be more frequent and more efficiently-loaded trains. It will also be possible to improve speeds, though it will not be easy to beat even the existing speed records on conventional railways. In 1954 the French National Railways ran an electric locomotive hauling three coaches at 151 m.p.h., and have repeated this performance with two different types of locomotive. One, in March 1955, averaged 185 m.p.h. for seven miles, reaching a maximum of 205 m.p.h.

The pneumatic tyres which the railway borrowed from the motor vehicle are not the only example of inspirations and acquisitions taken from a competitor. It is comic, almost pathetically humorous, when the ponderous earth-bound railway train seeks to borrow from its soaring competitor, the aeroplane, and attempts in its turn to fly! Not, it is true, to rise into the air, but to fly along the gleaming steel rails drawn or driven by an airscrew! This happened about twenty years ago in the case of the so-called *Rail Zeppelin*, invented by the German engineer, Kruckenberg. Even the railway had become air-minded! Pitying smiles soon vanished, however, when the '*Zepp*' flew along the rails at 143 miles an hour, on an experimental run between Hamburg and Spandau, a Berlin suburb. The distance of 168 miles

A contemporary artist's sketch of the Newton Abbot station on the South Devon Railway, showing the track-pipes and (on the left) the pump-house. Passengers liked the atmospheric railway on account of its smooth running and freedom from smoke, sparks and coal-dust. The trains also ran very punctually, 790 keeping (or gaining) time in 884 trips.

The old atmospheric railway pumping-station at Totnes, Devon. *Below:* A section of the
track-pipe; many of these old pipes were later utilized as drain-pipes.

P

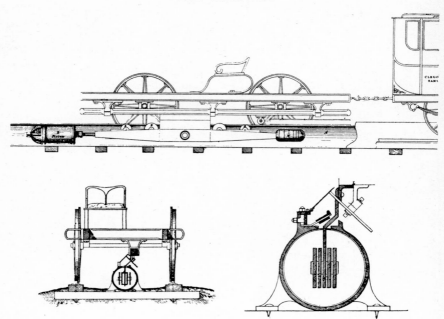

The 'engine' of the old South Devon railway. *Above:* The beam carrying the piston (left) and the counterpoise (right) is shown in the section of the pipe. The small wheels above the beam opened the air-seal and the little wheel below the engine-frame closed it again. *Below:* Cross-sections showing how the weather-guard protecting the flaps was raised.

was covered in one and three-quarter hours, which is an average speed of 96 m.p.h.

This was an interesting experiment, which, as a matter of fact, indicated the possibility of a motive power for rail-borne traffic independent both of friction and adhesion weight. No more hold on the rails was required: the propeller drew the whole train along. This propeller was, however, the real weak point of the design. In the air, and in the water, some form of bladed or reactive (screw or jet) propulsion is essential; but on solid ground the more familiar means available are to be preferred. After a while, the propeller was removed, and the *Rail Zeppelin* became an ordinary rail-car.

A much older attempt to eliminate the need for adhesion was made about 1830, when an 'atmospheric' railway was successfully tried out at Wormwood Scrubs, London. It was proposed to adopt this novel system for the Epsom extension of the London and Croydon railway, and an atmospheric railway was shortly afterwards built between Kingstown and Dalkey in Ireland, with the intention of extending it

The famous 'Schwebebahn', an electric suspension monorail connecting Barmen with Elberfeld in Western Germany. Overland congestion of traffic is relieved by supporting the track over existing roads and waterways. The car is here seen approaching along a stretch of the line over the river Wüpper.

to Bray if it proved satisfactory. The South Devon Railway directors were so favourably impressed by the Irish line that they instructed Isambard Kingdom Brunel, the great pioneer railway engineer, to install the air-propulsion system on the line from Exeter to Teignmouth. This was done in 1847, and the line was extended to Newton Abbot the following year, the total of forty miles of atmospheric track being in regular use for about eight months.

The principle of air-propulsion was simple. A cast-iron pipe fifteen inches in diameter was laid along the track midway between the two rails. There was a continuous slot in the upper side of the pipe, and a metal plate fixed to the underside of the driving-vehicle entered the pipe through the slot. Inside the pipe the plate was attached to a beam carrying a piston on its forward end and a counterpoise on its rear end. For the whole distance between the train and its destination the slot in the pipe was closed by a greased leather flap, and the air was removed from this section of the pipe by powerful stationary pumps situated beside the line at intervals of about five miles. The vacuum in the pipe drew the piston forward and so pulled the train along.

A simple mechanism beneath the driving-vehicle—it cannot be called an engine—opened the slot to make way for the plate, at the same time admitting air behind the piston and so making the vacuum effective. As the vehicle passed it automatically closed and sealed the pipe again in preparation for the return run. The pumping engines were started up in turn as the train became due, and ceased work on its passing. The driving-vehicle itself was a mere platform on wheels carrying a single chair for the guard. He did not in any sense 'drive' the train; he was there only to attend to emergencies. On this remarkable line trains weighing 100 tons were commonly pulled at 35 m.p.h., but light trains sometimes reached 68 m.p.h.

Modern experiments in suspension railways suggest that it is in this direction that the highest speeds will eventually be attained. The object is to combine the high speed of the aeroplane with the precision, punctuality and independence of weather which the railway already enjoys. The idea of suspending a train from a single overhead rail is not new. Its chief attraction is that only *one* rail is necessary, but the need for lightness demands an external source of power, such as electricity, or else a very light engine driving a propeller. The well-known monorail connecting the German towns of Barmen and Elberfeld first proposed in 1894 by Eugen Langen of Cologne, is an electrically-driven suspension railway the single car of which is capable of high speed. This is a monorail system that has been tested and proved in practice, and similar railways with overhead wheels hooked on to a single rail have been used in many places for the transport of goods.

As the centre of gravity of the Elberfeld rail car lies *beneath* the rail, the car is stable whether the machinery is in motion of not. This gives the occupants of the car a greater feeling of security than they might have on certain other varieties of monorailway, in which the car is

The old mono-railway between Listowel and Ballybunion. As the picture shows, the principle used here is the same as in the Cologne track of 1952 (see picture opposite). The idea of a single rail persists stubbornly, because there is something fundamentally sound about it.

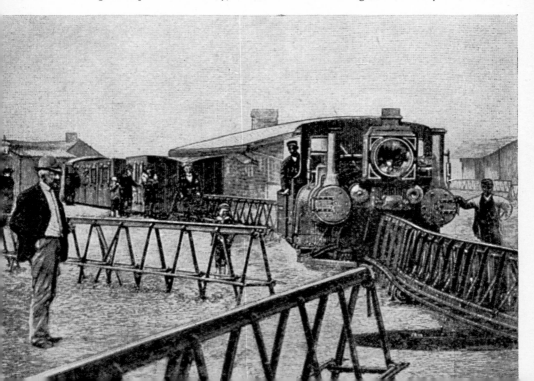

A monorailway, a model slightly under half size, was tried out in the vicinity of Cologne on the 8th October, 1952. A rail on a concrete girder supported by pillars takes the weight of the train, which rides astride the girder, so to speak. To prevent them from toppling over, the carriages are supported by four rails, two on each side of the concrete girder.

balanced on *top* of the rail. It must be admitted that the sight of a car standing on one row of wheels, like a man on one leg, is quite alarming when nothing can be seen to hold the car in equilibrium. In one experimental type balance is secured by means of a large, heavy gyroscope mounted in the car. So long as the gyroscope is kept spinning at a sufficient speed the car is perfectly stable, but when such a train is passing over a deep ravine on a single narrow rail not unlike a tight-rope, the passengers would really have to have a rock-like faith in mechanical theory to be able to enjoy the experience!

The first patent for this kind of monorail was taken out in 1903 by the Briton, Louis Brennan. However, his idea for 'giving stability with the help of a gyroscope to carriages which were naturally unstable', though it worked well enough, was not considered 100 per cent safe. If the power fails in an ordinary train it usually comes safely to a stand-still, but if the power failed in a gyroscopically stabilized train, nothing could prevent a terrible disaster. It was also uneconomical, for power had to be expended on the gyroscope as well as on driving the train along, and the Brennan monorail is never likely to be revived.

It is, of course, possible to keep a monorail car upright by giving it direct support, such as by means of a guide-rail at the top, or the train may be allowed to run in a deep groove with supporting rails along the side-walls, against which rollers fixed to the carriages can run—as was proposed by Lake as early as 1893. Yet another method of balancing a monorail train is that known as the 'riding' principle. In this, the single rail is raised on trestles, and *two* trains are used, one on each side of the trestles, but both being slung from the same central 'saddle' which carries a single row of wheels. They hang down on each side like pannier-bags, and balance each other.

This idea was first demonstrated at Lyons in 1872, and was developed further by the Spanish engineer Lartigue in the 1880's. It led finally to the Ballybunion railway, which ran in Ireland in 1887 and is shown on p. 244. These early ideas of trestles and the various types of guide-rail did not, however, come into general use, and presently they were forgotten. They lay dormant for seventy years, but now they have reappeared in a new stabilized monorail which has been built experimentally to half-scale near Cologne, with the financial support of the Swede, Axel Wenner-Gren. The riding principle is used, the car being —so to speak—cut into from below so that the lower half of it is in two separate parts, and it can thus sit astride a rail carried on a narrow concrete beam mounted on trestles.

The picture on p. 245 shows that the car is shaped like an aeroplane fuselage. This streamlining is deliberate, for the train will in one sense travel like an aeroplane through the air. The cross-section is almost circular and each of the wheels is directly coupled to an electric motor. The rail and the wheels come approximately in the centre of the circular cross-section of the car. Directly above them is the floor of the passenger cabin. Beneath, there are what we might call two cellars, hanging down one on each side of the rail.

Since the car is supported at or close to its centre of gravity, it will not be more stable than the plank of wood in a seesaw. A gentleman on the left side of the carriage who moved over to say "How do you do" to a lady on the right side would get little pleasure from the encounter, for the car would simply turn over. Perhaps gentlemen should not be encouraged to do such things, but the punishment does seem rather excessive. All things considered, the car must be prevented from seesawing. This is done by two rows of horizontal wheels on each side, and these are in contact with rails on the sides of the concrete beam. The car rides like a horseman who presses his thighs against the sides of his horse. The curious thing is that this railway, which prides itself on being a single-rail railway, actually has more rails than usual—five to be exact! But this is really a quibble, because the weight is taken

Railway vehicle or road vehicle—either is right. This is not an 'either-or' solution, but a true dual purpose vehicle. On the highway, it runs as a road vehicle, like any ordinary bus; where the railway tracks start it receives new wheels, a generator set and driving motor, and continues on its way as a diesel rail-car. This German experiment is one of a series, showing an interesting tendency towards a merger, obliterating the differences between road and rail transport. It is no longer the passenger who 'changes', but the transport vehicle. The passenger remains peacefully in his seat; hardly noticing whether he is travelling 'by rail', or 'by bus'.

by one rail only, and in principle the Cologne track is a true monorail. It will be interesting to follow the further experiments with this railway, especially when a full-scale model is built. The experiments are being carried out with great thoroughness and speeds of 190 m.p.h. have been anticipated.

Even if one or the other of these projects is given a practical trial somewhere, it would be wrong to identify them with the true principle of the railway. What is of interest in forecasting the trend of future railway development is the possibility of new, revolutionary suggestions. In one respect, modern developments call for a revision of ideas and first principles: the railway is not the strait-jacketed, rigid organization that it is so often thought to be.

War to the knife has been declared on the railway by its younger rivals, but the railway has by no means surrendered unconditionally or tamely; it has rather adopted and realized ideas first developed by its competitors, and has incorporated them in its own system and methods to the utmost possible extent. Diesel drive, bold advances in speed, streamlining, modern freight handling—the railway has not been insensitive to these suggestions from the rival camps, nor has it rejected them out of hand; on the contrary, it has used them to further and stimulate its own, ageing organism.

The railway has abandoned the old-established belief that a long train is the best train. It is freely using single vehicles. In the rivalry between road and rail, it is remarkable how the road vehicles are acquiring more wheels and are becoming bigger and bigger, being equipped with sleeping facilities and made to run to regular time-tables with proper stations and halting points—in fact, are increasingly copying and following railway operating methods and techniques, whereas the railway is in many ways developing in the opposite direction. The long trains are shrinking to rail-cars, the steam engine no longer predominates, the internal-combustion engine has made a place for itself, though in regard to wheels, the road vehicles' pneumatic tyres have not proved ideal for use under railway vehicles.

Otherwise, the railway vehicle is beginning to resemble what used to be the typical motor-car. The No-Man's Land between these two forms of transport is becoming increasingly smaller and narrower, as their ideas and developments tend to merge, and there are signs and tokens heralding the birth of a new 'road-rail/rail-road' vehicle, running at will on either track. It may set off as a road vehicle, and with a slight wheel-adjustment continue along the railway track; then, making another quick change, it may arrive at its destination on the road again.

It may be asked, what then remains of the essentials of a railway, as already defined and discussed? It is not easy to answer this question decisively. Hitherto, the problem of road *versus* rail transport has been regarded as an economic rivalry in which there are two 'sides'. This conception does not reach the roots of the matter. The reference to

It has been calculated that something of the order of 9 million man-hours per week are expended in the United States on loading and unloading motor vehicles; much of this time, on transferring goods from road to rail and *vice versa*. The closed motor van shown here has a special hydraulic jack to raise or lower its floor to the floor level of a goods platform or railway goods truck, and thus assist loading and unloading.

'sides' tends to obscure the true problem—the interest of the traffic and of the general public which this traffic serves. From the pure traffic aspect, there should be no 'sides', only 'partners'; the trend should be towards a general fusion, in which neither road nor rail continues to exist as an independent, rival form of transport.

There is, for example, a new development in the technique of modern transport which perhaps represents the first step towards such amalgamation. In the overland carriage of goods the following scheme is often operated. The load is picked up by road vehicle, taken by road to a railway station, transferred to a goods truck, hauled by a locomotive along a railway line, transferred again to a road vehicle, and 'carted home' (as railway goods traffic terminology has it) by the latter. It has been estimated that in the United States 8,628,000 man-hours per week are spent in loading and unloading railway vehicles. Faced with this astounding figure, and bearing in mind that man-hours cost money, it is natural to wonder whether such transfers from vehicle to vehicle are really necessary. Obviously they are necessary, it may be said, if both road and rail transport are to be used, but only because the different vehicles run on different kinds of wheels. It should not be beyond the ingenuity of man to devise a vehicle which shall be neither a road-motor nor a rail-car, but a combination of both.

So far, we have arrived at the wheel-less container—a large box resembling the body of a covered goods van. This box-body is loaded with goods and transferred as a unit from road to rail, or from rail to road. This so-called 'container' method is now being used on a larger and larger scale. In its stark simplicity it represents a revolution in transport methods. Such containers need not take the simple form of square boxes. They can be built in any form for any special purposes, such as a large tank equipped with temperature-control arrangements, for transporting milk. Such milk-containers are already used in France. The essential feature of such container-bodies is that they shall fit the undercarriages of both road and railway vehicles, and in each case form an integral, complete vehicle.

A further development which is having an extensive vogue in the United States is the so-called 'piggyback' method of transporting road lorries on their rubber-tyred wheels. They are run two at a time on to long flat wagons, which are marshalled in long-distance freight trains. The lorries are brought to the railway by petrol tractors, and on arrival at their terminal station are drawn off by tractors on to the road, and worked through to destination, so providing door-to-door transport of a very simple kind.

This development of a 'container service' represents such a close

The gleaming ribbons of steel represent stability—the permanent way, which will last our time.

interlinking of road and rail traffic interests as to constitute, in actual
fact, a third form of land transport in which both the preceding forms
are indistinguishably merged. We are witnessing a vast process of
mutual adaptation, and a way will be found to give all three forms of
land transport their just and natural share in a world-wide system
of traffic-handling on the most rational and economic principles.

In this process of adaptation the railway has suffered, and will yet
suffer, some remarkable and far-reaching changes and transformations,
and this with a rapidity and flexibility surprising for such an old-
established institution. Many innovations are yet to come, but in one
respect the railway will remain the 'iron road' so long as the sound of
a train is still to be heard on earth. The fundamental conception of
the two gleaming ribbons of rail on which the traffic runs has faithfully
persisted, and will continue to persist from the first to the last days of
the railway. These bright lines of steel have spanned continents, have
been the pioneers of trade, industry, and common civilization, and it
is their development which has caused our world to contract before
men's eyes into an increasingly compact, united community. Rolling
stock fashions and types change and disappear; motive power changes,
systems and methods are transformed almost out of recognition; all
goes into the melting pot under the all-impelling law of scientific and
technical progress. Alone, the iron road remains. The two bright lines
of steel are indeed a 'permanent way'.

INDEX

Page numbers in italics refer to illustrations.

ACKNOWLEDGMENT

Acknowledgments are due to the *Meccano Magazine* for the coloured *Frontispiece* and to the following for illustrations on the pages indicated. British Railways (pp. 16, 56, 131, 139, 140, 232, 240, 241, 242), Central Library, Croydon (p. 10), Fox Photos (pp. 50, 103), London Transport (pp. 132, 138). Pullman Car Company (p. 209), *The Times* (p. 133).